CHILDREN
OF THE
KINGDOM

BRIDGING GENETICS AND ISLAM TO SAVE THE NEWBORNS OF SAUDI ARABIA

DR. TERRENCE R. DOLAN

First Edition

S. **Woodhouse** Books

Chicago ∎ Milwaukee

Children of the Kingdom:
Bridging Genetics and Islam to Save the Children of Saudi Arabia
Terrence R. Dolan, Ph.D.

Published September 2016 by:

S. **Woodhouse** Books

S. Woodhouse Books, an imprint of Everything Goes Media
www.everythinggoesmedia.com

Publisher's Cataloging-In-Publication Data
(Prepared by The Donohue Group, Inc.)

Names: Dolan, Terrence R.
Title: Children of the kingdom : bridging genetics and Islam to save the new-
    borns of Saudi Arabia / Dr. Terrence R. Dolan.
Description: [Chicago, Illinois] : S. Woodhouse Books, an imprint of Everything
    Goes Media, LLC, 2016. | Includes bibliographical references and index.
Identifiers: LCCN 2016940669 | ISBN 978-1-893121-87-4 | ISBN 978-1-893121-
    83-6 (ebook)
Subjects: LCSH: Dolan, Terrence R. | Genetic disorders--Religious aspects--Is-
    lam. | Genetics--Research--Saudi Arabia. | Islam and science--Saudi Arabia.
    | Consanguinity (Islamic law) | Saudi Arabia--Social life and customs.
Classification: LCC RA645.G4 D65 2016 | DDC 616.042--dc23

20 19 18 17 16   10 9 8 7 6 5 4 3 2 1

This book is dedicated to children born with diseases and disabilities—as we move towards a peaceful world, may they be a productive and joyful part of it.

CONTENTS

Part I

Part II

Part III

PART I

The Waisman Center, University of Wisconsin, Madison.

CHAPTER 1
Opportunity Rings

The call that jangles your office phone precisely at 9 a.m. on a Monday morning clues you that the caller has waited, and not so patiently, all weekend—watched the numbers change from 8:59 to 9:00 before dialing. Opportunity doesn't knock. It rings.

That morning, outside the window of my ringing phone, was an idyllic, warm central Wisconsin spring day, 2000. The last vestiges of a long Midwestern winter finally were dissipating. Spring in a university town has a predictable rhythm. Each year, as nature comes back to life, students eagerly approach their departures from the University of Wisconsin to embark on new summers and new adventures. I remembered what that felt like, but distantly.

I had been a professor and now was a neuroscientist and the director of the university's Waisman Center for Developmental Disabilities, one of the largest centers in the world on the research and development of children. It had been decades since I was uncertain about my path.

I answered the phone.

"Dolan here. May I help you?"

The voice on the other end was crisp. "Dr. Terrence Dolan, my name is Peggy Johnson and I'm calling from Los Angeles. I work for an executive search agency," she went on, "and am calling on behalf of an international client. The purpose of my phone call is to assist this client in his search for a person with your knowledge and skills, to participate in a major, long-term health research project outside the United States."

That's quite a mouthful, especially for 7 a.m. Pacific Time, I thought.

"Ms....Johnson?" I asked. "Did you say your name was Johnson? How did you get my name and phone number?"

An almost imperceptible chuckle at my skepticism escaped her professional veneer. "Dr. Dolan, let me assure you this phone call is the result of substantial prior research on the part of our firm. We've already determined you are a person in whom we have specific interest. We have spoken with a number of experts in child neuroscience, both in the United States and abroad, and your name has come up repeatedly in those conversations."

Well, this told me next to nothing. As I tried to process what she was saying, every potential scam and dubious motive popped into my head. I'll blame caffeine deprivation—my coffee was cooling, still untouched— for why my mind wandered to consider just how far cable companies would go to get you to switch. What did she *really* want? Who *was* this client? Was Peggy Johnson even her real name?

"Whoa, Ms. Johnson! This is a lot of information coming from an unfamiliar source. Who are the people you've talked to and where is this project of yours?"

She didn't hesitate or vary her professional, firm intonation. "Dr. Dolan, until you've expressed at least preliminary interest in our inquiries, I'm afraid I'm not at liberty to divulge that information. However, I would be *happy* to continue these conversations at that time. I can assure you my client is a reputable entity and that the project is one we believe you'd find most interesting."

She was still in pursuit mode, and I was certainly intrigued, but I'm a researcher and always gather my facts before making decisions. She didn't stand a chance. "I'm afraid this conversation is beyond my Monday morning capabilities, Ms. Johnson," I said. "I'm going to have to decline this offer. I'm very happy here at the University of Wisconsin and I'm committed to my present work."

"I understand, Dr. Dolan. Please let me know if you have any questions or change your mind," she added. But before Johnson could offer up her contact information I had mentally moved on.

As I set the phone back on the cradle, my hand lingered for a moment, as if I could coax some genie with answers out of a bottle.

In the day's busyness, it was only during the odd moment or two of down time that my thoughts ventured back to her call.

Later that evening, my wife Mary Ann and I visited our neighbors Tom and Harriet Fisher for a cookout. We had known them for some time, and our get-togethers around the backyard grill were a regular feature of our warm-weather evenings. We started our usual routine for outdoor and indoor tasks. Tom and I cracked open a couple of beers, set up the picnic table, and heated the coals; Mary Ann and Harriet prepared salads and sides.

That night, as Tom spread smoldering coals around the grill, I mentioned my conversation with Peggy Johnson, "if that was even her name!" I added.

"That's strange," Tom said. "How in the hell did they get ahold of you?"

"God only knows," I said.

"I mean…what kind of work do you do that would be interesting to some mystery guys overseas?"

Harriett called out, "Hey, are you talking about that phone call?" as she and Mary Ann walked out onto the deck. "What was *that* all about, Terry?"

"Well, OK," I said, returning to Tom's question as he shifted his focus to maneuvering hamburgers on the grill. "I don't really know what *these* mystery guys want, but I know a kind of project it *might* be. A while back, I worked as an outside reviewer on a project that took place in Iran. All around the Persian Gulf, there's an ongoing problem with the health of newborns. They're born prematurely and often have birth defects; an *unusual* number of birth defects. Year after year experts come in to try to diagnose the cause, but no one really has any idea what's going on."

"Like, what? Whether it was genetic, maybe?" Tom offered.

"Right, it could be," I agreed, "or it could be an environmental issue, or some mysterious other issue, or some combination. So the tasks for the project were to figure out the cause and a way to fix the problem. I don't know, but that may be the kind of work this mystery call is about."

That seemed to satisfy Tom and Harriet, and we let the subject drop for the moment. But the call, the anonymous client, and the international intrigue were just too cloak-and-dagger for anyone to resist. As our burgers were replaced by homemade peach cobbler, the morning's call came up again. Tom said, poking at dessert, "I don't know. It just seems so strange. I mean, the fact that she couldn't reveal her client or the nature of the project. Do you have a secret life we don't know about, Terry?" He laughed. "I bet you get calls like this all the time!"

I shook my head chuckling. "No, I definitely do not!"

"And you really have no idea what they were calling about?" he asked.

"Just what I was guessing at earlier. Some kind of large-scale health problem they think I could..." I paused. "They think I could help with."

I stared for a few beats into a flickering citronella candle, lost in the possibility. *What if,* I thought...*what if I really might be able to help?*

"I mean," Harriett jumped in, "granted, you don't really know very much about this, but if you *were* interested, you might have to work or even move overseas!"

"We'd have to think about the house," Mary Ann said, agreeing with the improbability of the call turning into anything. "The kids. Terry's work at the University."

I nodded along with the others. It was fun to *talk* about the possibility, but regardless of what the problem was, how could we even consider moving abroad? *Us,* with four children and five grandchildren, and at *this* stage of our lives?

The phone call needled at me for a few days. Was this a legitimate project? Could I really help? Where in the world was this mystery client? If the opportunity arose, could we pick up and move somewhere? After a while, usual day-to-day matters drove the mystery call's place from my mind.

The phone rang again. "Dr. Dolan, this is Peggy Johnson, from Los Angeles. We spoke a few weeks ago?" said the voice on the phone. This time, I smiled.

"I remember you, Ms. Johnson," I said. "Actually, I was wondering if you might call again."

"My client was very insistent that I did," she said, amiably.

"I haven't changed my mind, but I'd be lying if I said I wasn't a little curious," I confessed.

I could hear her smile on the other end of the line. "Well, that's certainly a start."

"But look, I have nothing to go on here. I have a lot on my plate. I need to know what this is all about."

"I'm sure you understand I can't yet go deeply into specifics, Dr. Dolan, and I do apologize for that. But I can say that the project will be very large in scope and could have serious significance for human health."

"Is it safe to assume that you're contacting me about my work developing research centers for childhood diseases and disabilities?"

For the first time, Peggy Johnson hesitated. "That...Yes, that would be correct."

"And where do I fit in to this project?"

"My client sees you as an excellent candidate to create and run this project," she said, "in every aspect."

"Well, you definitely have my attention, Peggy," I said, switching to her first name. One of my deputy administrators was loitering at my door, fussing with a notebook and conspicuously trying to look inconspicuous. "Hey, look, I really have to run right now," I gestured to my associate to come in, "but please, give me a call next week and let's continue the conversation."

"I'll do that," she said.

That night, before we turned out the lights, Mary Ann and I tried to guess where this client might be.

"Perhaps it's in Africa," Mary Ann said. "The health situation in so many countries there is dire. You could do a lot of good."

She had a point. But without more information, the possible locations were global...and limitless.

Intermittently, conversations with Peggy Johnson continued. Progress was slow. I felt that each time I learned only infinitesimally more. It was summertime by then, and many of the university's students had left to begin their adventures.

It was a pleasant distraction to imagine an adventure of my own. I was doubtful I would seriously consider this project, but the more I talked to Peggy Johnson, the more I began to think of it as a possibility.

Finally, in what must have been the seventh or eighth L.A. to Madison phone call, Peggy and I struck a deal.

"Let me make sure I have this right," I said. "You'll tell me who your mysterious client is and where the project is located if I agree to participate in a videoconference with him to hear what he has to say."

"Correct," was her reply.

"All right, Ms. Johnson," I said with renewed formality. We were, after all, negotiating a contract of sorts. I rolled my chair in, hands folded on my desk. Things were moving forward. "We have a deal."

CHAPTER 2
The Coffee Server's Son

*I*n *an artificially cooled office, in a bustling and wealthy city, in a country of sand and sun, a young man pours his employer a cup of coffee from a silver urn called a dallah. Ibrahim is a coffee-serving employee working late into the relatively cool night. Unlike many of his childhood friends, he has been granted gainful work that enables him to support, albeit modestly, a wife and child.*

His boss dismisses him with a gesture of his hand. The young man turns toward a commotion he hears—a familiar voice in the street below. He peers down and sees his neighbor looking up, waving frantically for him to come outside.

"Something is wrong!" the neighbor shouts. "It's Fatima, your wife. Come quickly!"

Ibrahim is sprinting now, his coffee urn, his boss, his job far behind. He has long since outrun his neighbor, the messenger of what can only be bad news. His sandals slap the pavement. One terrible possibility after another torments him. He can't get home quickly enough, yet he never wants to arrive. Until he does, the reality of what awaits is still only a possibility.

The boulevards of this desert city glow with street and office lights and rumble with the noise of heavy traffic. All this soon falls behind him. The streets narrow and darken. The sidewalk here is cracked and crumbling. Ahead, he hears the sound of men yelling. Are they yelling his wife's name?

As he approaches, he sees a crowd of men clustered in front of his door, hands on their heads, frustrated with helplessness. None are related to Fatima so they may not enter the house as no adult male relative was home. Thankfully, several of their wives are with Fatima, trying to comfort her. Ibrahim darts inside. The wives depart. In the tiny back room, his wife kneels, cradling their four-month-old son in her arms.

Ibrahim and Fatima were married fifteen months ago—an arranged marriage as is customary. First cousins, they have known each other all their lives. Now husband and wife, they work to meet the demands of their new family. But all has not been well. From the moment their son Aziz greeted the world, something was not quite as it should be. The boy's color is dull and pale. They eagerly wait for his eyes to meet their own, for his tiny fist to wrap around their fingers. They continue to wait. Is it simply the worry of new parents that they imagine their son's movements as sometimes clumsy and uncontrolled? That Aziz seems to be weaker than other babies? Do they read too much into normal childhood rashes?

Catching his breath, Ibrahim listens as his wife explains that from a sound sleep, their son had begun to twitch uncontrollably, jerking and seizing. The child in her arms shows no evidence of this trauma. He is asleep.

Ibrahim has heard of such conditions before. He recalls the youngest daughter of the fruit vendor had an affliction like this. And the toddler nephew of the school teacher. He does not know the cause of these maladies, only they ended in an early death—and he is terrified.

Panic gives way to relief as baby Aziz awakes and begins to stir. In this bubble of solace, Ibrahim and Fatima hurry to assure themselves this was just a fluke, a singular event, but each knows, and does not say, that in this country their son's ailments are an unalterable fact of life. It is only a matter of time.

Elsewhere in the city, eight kilometers and a world away, a few men sit at a conference table built of solid cherry and polished to a high shine. The table holds a teetering stack of papers, nearly a foot high. The paper tower moves silently as Dr. Al Dosaary slides it gently in front of his visitor.

The elegant man glances back at the doctor, peels the top page off the stack and scans it, holding the sheet with both hands. He sits stiffly, uncomfortably—a rarity for him, Dr. Al Dosaary suspects. This is a dignitary accustomed to comfort. Silently, expectantly, the physician watches him read as does every other person in the room. The medical center's

*staff stands in line down the long side of the conference room, politely
and pensively, hands primly folded. The cluster of the visitor's entourage
stands across from them on the other side of the room. After what feels
like hours, the visitor waves his hand toward the stack of papers. "And
these are all . . . ?"*

*The doctor pauses a moment, ascertaining if his visitor has finished
speaking. "Yes, these are the medical reports on birth defects we have
collected from individual physicians throughout the Kingdom, Your
Highness."*

"But this doesn't reflect all the birth defects," the royal visitor says.

*"No." Dr. Al Dosaary looks down at a smudge on the table in front
of him.*

"Just the—what did you call them?"

*"They are often referred to as inborn errors of metabolism, Your Roy-
al Highness," Dr. Al Dosaary, emboldened by the compassion in the
Prince's voice, raises his eyes. "And these are only from a few hospitals
in a few major cities, Your Highness. We have no way to properly estimate how many cases we have even in the city, let alone the villages,
or in rural areas. Most countries in the world have developed national
screening programs. But here in our homeland we have but one screening program that has been initiated and it is very modest in scope.*

*The Prince gazes for a moment at the reports stacked high before him,
then shakes his head with sadness. "There is no change nor strength save
through Allah," he murmurs. Turning to Dr. Al Dosaary he asks, "Can
you explain to me what these diseases are? Briefly. I'm not a scientist, but
it's important that I understand."*

*"Of course," the physician pauses again. He has not considered how
to provide an entry-level lecture on genetic diseases—let alone in two
minutes, and certainly not for a prominent member of the Royal Family.
"Well, Your Highness, our genes are found in most cells of our body and
are grouped into structures called chromosomes. We have twenty-three
pairs of chromosomes; within each pair, we receive one chromosome
from each parent.*

"If something is wrong with one of the genes in these chromosomes…"

"Wrong, how?" the Prince interrupts.

*"Our genes—our genes are like a recipe. The body reads them and
uses each gene as a guide to make one kind of protein. And of course*

there are many, many different proteins in the body.

"If something is wrong with the recipe on one chromosome, but not the other, it's sometimes not a problem. The body makes enough of the protein by following the recipe from the other chromosome in that pair. But if there something wrong with both…"

"Then there's exists no good recipe to follow," the Prince concludes.

"Exactly. These diseases are the result of the body failing to produce a certain protein, or producing a wrong or misshapen one."

"So many proteins," the Prince says with wonder in his voice, "and yet in the absence of just one… just one… we end up…" He waves his hand toward the stack of reports again.

"Yes, Your Highness."

The Prince nods again, smooths his long white robe over his lap, and stands. Immediately, his entourage and the medical center's staff stiffen, coming to attention.

"I'll speak with my family, see what we can do," the Prince says with a sigh, and gives Dr. Al Dosaary a small, formal kiss on both cheeks. "Thank you very much. You have taught me a great deal. Al Hamdulilla!

"Thanks be to Allah," repeats Dr. Al Dosaary, and means it sincerely. An untold number of children—literally an inestimable number of children, babies, really—were suffering and dying in every part of the Kingdom, and had been for years. Maybe now, finally, this would change.

CHAPTER 3
The Royal Family

"Prince *who?!*" I exclaimed, much louder than I intended, into the ears of poor Peggy Johnson. I skidded backwards in my chair and a stack of final exams fell to the floor as I all-but-shouted, "You have *got* to be kidding me!"

I couldn't wait to tell Mary Ann, but wanted to see the look on her face.

"So..." I asked my wife, as casually as I could as I walked in the door that night, "how would you feel about having a pet camel?"

She stopped and fixed me with a look that said, *All right, Dolan, explain this one.*

I opened up my briefcase on the kitchen table and pulled out my notes from the call. "The client Ms. Johnson works for," I announced, reading it slowly, "is Prince Sultan bin Salman bin Abdul Aziz of Saudi Arabia."

A moment passed. Then another. Finally: "Wow!" I couldn't tell if she was more impressed with the client or the fact that I pronounced his name.

"So the project is in Saudi Arabia," I continued.

"Yes, I gathered that," she said.

We were living in a university town in the heartland. Mary Ann and I never had occasion to mix with royalty. I don't think we ever even met aristocracy. So, needless to say, the caliber of the client was unfamiliar. Even so, if it had been, say, a member of the British Royal Family, at least we would have had some knowledge, some comfort with the culture. A Saudi Arabian prince?! This was uncharted territory.

We did our best to stay on top of the news, but Mary Ann and I had only the most superficial impressions of the country. Our first thoughts were desert, heat, sun, oil, wealth, conservatism. We spent the rest of the evening, through dinner and after, discussing this new information; turning it over, breaking it apart, envisioning it. What would it be like to visit Saudi Arabia? How long would we go? And most important of all, what could the issue be, a health threat so serious that a prince had sought me out halfway around the world? We were captivated, amazed. As we discussed and deliberated, Mary Ann brought over our laptop and we investigated as much as we could about the country. More about that later.

It wasn't long before she looked up with a twinkle in her eye and said, "You know... you *do* have that sabbatical program, right? You could take advantage of it. "It was true. The University has had a fairly straightforward system so tenured faculty can take time off for career-enhancing activities. It was not so much time "off" as time away from campus.

"And besides," I added, "I'm not getting any younger here." Mary Ann smiled. I was sixty years old. Some would say (the angel on *one* of my shoulders, for example) that sixty was no time to uproot ourselves to an utterly foreign place: a desert monarchy with a hostile climate and norms we couldn't begin to imagine. The one on the *other* shoulder whispered rather insistently that perhaps this was the *ideal* time for us to go!

The more Mary Ann and I talked, the more we came to realize this was likely the best chance we were going to get for a grand adventure. Our health was good, and, let's be honest, anything that's challenging at sixty would be only harder at seventy. Our four children had left the nest. Our youngest daughter was in college, and the others had started professional lives and families of their own. Far from being crazy or too late for a move like this, it was actually the first chance in nearly forty years of marriage to begin such an adventure!

Contemplating the possibility reminded us both of an excursion we took more than twenty years earlier; during a one-year sabbatical as a visiting professor to Erlangen, Germany. The whole family was able to go, and all these years later, it remained a favorite family memory.

Here now was the possibility of a Saudi Arabian enterprise. Faster than you could say "Prince Sultan bin Salman bin Abdul Aziz," Mary Ann and I started enumerating everything we'd have to learn before we could seriously consider taking this on. We had little information about the project, so we thought about ourselves: How long would we have to stay in Saudi Arabia to make a meaningful contribution? What sort of expenses would we have? Where and how would we live? For that matter, was it even safe to live there? Could we do this without speaking a word of Arabic?

I assumed my prospective employers had many questions for me, and I certainly had many for them. I called Peggy Johnson and scheduled our videoconference for just a few days later, near the end of July.

"Good morning, Dr. Dolan," said one of three men in white.

I was sitting alone in a private, off-campus videoconferencing facility. In a strip mall nobody visited. On a street few traveled. No one but Mary Ann and a few very close friends knew about my tentative Saudi Arabian affair. It was too early in the courtship for publicity.

On the screen in front of me, I saw a panel of four men lined up at a conference table. One, clearly not Saudi, wore a western business suit and introduced himself as William Cornish, an expat consultant from Canada, who was assisting in the search. The men in white wore cotton robes with a cloth draped over their heads secured with cords. Later, I learned that the robes were called *thoubes*, the head covering a *ghutra* and the cord an *ekaal*.

"I am Naif," the man onscreen said, "One of Prince Sultan's personal assistants."

Just then I realized just how long it had been since my last job interview. A touch of nerves had left breakfast untouched, and I was drinking quickly from a water bottle I bought at the 7-11 next door.

Following an extremely formal set of introductions, Naif proceeded with suffocating professionalism. "Dr. Dolan, I would first like to outline our objectives for this call. Naturally, we wish to learn more about you. But most critically, we wish to impress upon you the urgency of the problem we are bringing to your attention. On the basis of your past work, we trust that once the scale and magnitude of the situation become apparent to you, you will share our urgency.

"Regardless," he finished, "we wish to insist that these discussions remain confidential."

"Of course," I said, my own tone aligning itself with Naif's formality. "As you're no doubt aware, and as I'm happy to discuss further, I've been involved with very large-scale and delicate health issues before."

A series of *pro forma* questions about me followed. It was hard to imagine Peggy's search firm had left any of my professional experience to chance, so it was becoming increasingly clear that this call was about selling *me* on the project, more than vice versa. The sales pitch was slow in coming. My interlocutors were cordial but inscrutable.

"What are your hobbies, Dr. Dolan?" Naif asked.

"Hobbies?" I was losing interest. "I'm quite fond of skiing, actually," I said, distractedly. "I spend as much time on the ski slopes as I can."

I could see Naif and the other Saudis smile. "You will understand," he said, "that skiing is somewhat less popular for us." It was a stilted attempt at a joke, but it managed to lighten the mood considerably.

With a change in course, and tone, Naif abruptly said, "Let me tell you what the Prince's concern is, Dr. Dolan."

I sat forward, attentive. *Finally.*

"Prince Sultan entertains a suspicion about the incidence of diseases among the children of our Kingdom," he began. Peggy Johnson had told me as much already. I knew they had sought me out for my familiarity with pediatric diseases. "Including both neonatal and childhood disease, the Prince believes that this incidence may be higher than it is in other nations."

The "may" struck me as odd, and I didn't think it was just his bureaucratic phrasing. Didn't they *know*? Weren't they keeping track of these things? I spent an instant searching for diplomatic phrasing. "How confident is he that the incidence is higher?" I asked.

Wrong query. "I am not in the habit of questioning the basis of His Highness's concerns," Naif replied briskly. "For me it is sufficient to know that the Prince feels it must be investigated."

I'm sure I gave Naif a disapproving look. Surely they had to know that any academic they hired—any professional scientist—especially a foreigner not beholden to the authority of the Saudi Royal Family, would question *everything,* his or her own conclusions most of all. If there wasn't a problem, there wasn't. And if there was, there was.

Without missing a beat, Naif continued. "Speaking in very general terms, we feel it is crucial first to determine the *extent* of the problem. Then, we would try to determine the cause. We understand diseases may be inherited. However, Prince Sultan also suspects that some regions of the country may be more prone to these diseases than others, so we wonder if some other factor may be in play."

I nodded, concurring with their logic so far. The Prince, or at least his spokesman, seemed to have at least a rudimentary understanding of the complex causes at the root of many diseases. For the "nature-versus-nurture" question—whether some diseases arise from genetics or from the environment—the answer, of course, is both. A person's genes or an environmental toxin may cause a disease, but oftentimes it's a combination. Genetic makeup may predispose a person to be more or less susceptible to environmental harms. This has long been an area of active research for scientists and physicians worldwide.

"Finally, of course," Naif continued, "once we understand the cause, we would like to develop a national strategy to correct it."

"Understood," I said. I had speculated about what health issue might be of such pressing interest to a prince of Saudi Arabia that he would seek me. Finding the underlying causes of childhood diseases and a way to address them certainly justified their urgency.

"Admittedly," Naif conceded, "I am not competent to discuss these issues in greater detail. Should you choose to arrange a visit to the Kingdom, however, I assure you that relevant personnel, and Prince Sultan himself, will be able to elaborate on them."

A visit? I thought, reflecting on how much longer my passport would be valid. Throat dry, brow growing damp, I reached for my nearly empty water bottle. My body seemed to be catching up to my brain, responding to the notion of a desert trip. The possibilities were beginning to feel unmistakably real.

Hurrying home from the videoconference center, I called out to Mary Ann while I was swinging open the kitchen door. I could hardly wait to see her and wanted to be sure she'd hear me from the attic to the cellar.

"Geez, Terry, I'm right here," she said from not ten feet away. She was sitting at the kitchen table, smiling indulgently. "You sure sound excited."

"Have I got a story for you!" I said, sitting across from her, my coat and tie still on. She slid over the glass of wine that she'd already poured for me.

I told her everything: the four men including the three in thoubes, Naif's stilted demeanor and modest joke, my nerves. And then, coming to the important bits, about the mysterious illnesses that may be afflicting children of the Kingdom of Saudi Arabia.

"Do they think the problem is genetic?" she asked.

"Strictly speaking, they're not even sure they *have* a problem which surprised me. They must not track health statistics very well."

"And isn't it such a wealthy country?"

"I think we're going to have a lot to learn here," I answered. Thinking of Naif's response when I questioned their data, I shook my head. "Anyway, it sounds like the first part of the work is going to be bread-and-butter epidemiology. If they don't even know how many kids are sick, and they might not, we've got to start there."

"Of course," she said.

"The second part is, if there is a problem, we figure out what's causing it. I have my suspicions already."

"What do you think it is?"

I was operating from CNN- and *Newsweek*-level knowledge. "I could be mistaken, but I'm pretty sure poverty in the region was near universal until after the War," I said. Mary Ann and I were the last of the generation that, when we said "the War," meant World War II. "That's when they first started exporting their oil, at least on a large scale. So until a generation or two ago, it was an isolated desert country full of poor people."

Mary Ann jumped on the thought. "So you think, maybe, there are a lot of genetic diseases . . ."

I finished. "The gene pool was homogeneous and they didn't mix much with outsiders. It could be. The region could be a place like Japan or Finland. Populations that isolate themselves by necessity or by choice tend to have higher levels of inborn disease."

"I remember that," she said, perhaps thinking back to nursing school. "Japanese people have diseases that don't exist anywhere else. A subset of Jews, too, I think."

"Ashkenazi, right. This is just a hypothesis. I didn't bring it up with Naif and the others. But it's something to keep in mind."

Mary Ann smiled, and I realized what I'd done. Before I'd signed a single paper or received a dollar, before even a handshake, I'd already jumped on the problem, trying to puzzle it out. I'd put on my investigator's hat without even noticing. Not because I had to or had given my word that I would, but because the problem existed. Like most scientists, what got me up in the morning wasn't the pursuit of fame and *certainly* not the pursuit of money. It was the hunt for understanding, the chase that ends in finding answers, in knowing something more deeply than anyone has before you. "Anyhow, I'm glad they're thinking of environmental factors too. They seem to understand that genetic makeup may just *predispose* people to having a disease, rather than outright giving it to them."

The question piqued my interest: Are Saudis more likely than others to be affected by genetic diseases activated by environmental factors? It would mean that Saudi Arabia could function like a natural laboratory for investigating the interplay between genes, the environment, and cultural factors. The country had a large, homogeneous gene pool, and it had some areas where diseases arose more frequently than in others. That setup could expose the environmental factors that were behind any number of diseases. I sipped my wine. Details still needed to be worked out, but I was eager to see Saudi Arabia for myself.

CHAPTER 4
Saudi Arabia 101

I knew very little about Saudi Arabia in 2000. From the Internet, here is a brief overview.

First, a map.

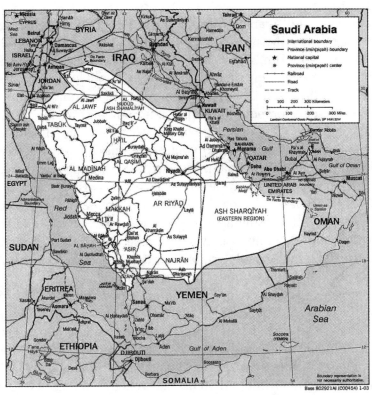

Map of Saudi Arabia. (*From worldofmaps.net, based on public domain image from the U.S. Central Intelligence Agency.*)

Saudi Arabia and the Arab Peninsula comprise a vast desert land. Studies of Western Civilization often romantically call it the Crossroads of History and the Cradle of Civilization. For centuries, it was a center for international trade, and during the 600s A.D. it was a major hub in the Coastal Route of the Silk Road, bearing riches from the East to the newly developing civilizations in the West. Arab intellectuals, particularly in the sciences—including mathematics, medical sciences, and architecture—made basic contributions for subsequent centuries of progress. Arabic influences reached around the world in architecture and other fields; in algebra, both the word and its techniques have Arabic sources.

The history of the Arab Peninsula is rich with intellectual achievement. Yet for much of the past 300 years, it has been marked by conflict and turmoil.

Leadership

The current Saudi Arabian ruling family, the Al Saud Dynasty, can be traced back to the tribe headed by Muhammad bin Saud, whose power dates back to 1744. "Bin" is translated as "son of." The Al Saud tribe was driven out of the Arab Peninsula in 1891 when another long-standing and powerful tribe, the Rashids, forced them into what is now Kuwait.

In 1902, the development of the present branch of the Saud tribe and the present country of Saudi Arabia began when a young Al Saud warrior, Abdul Aziz bin Saud, led a small contingent out of Kuwait to recapture land taken by the Rashids. That initial battle, well-known and celebrated in Saudi Arabia, occurred at the Masmak Fortress (the center of power in the Rashid Dynasty) in the central part of modern-day Riyadh. After three decades of fighting against other resident Sheikhs and tribes in the Kingdom, bin Saud and his warriors recaptured most of their original land. In 1932, he formally established the Kingdom of Saudi Arabia, named for the Saud family, and proclaimed himself King.

A key strategy used by the King to maintain power in the Kingdom was to marry the daughters of Sheikhs. Islam allows up to four wives simultaneously, and Abdul Aziz himself married and divorced numerous times, fathering children with twenty-two wives. Most records include forty-five sons and approximately fifty additional daughters. He died in 1953, leaving as many as 1,300 grandchildren! Today his progeny—some 20,000 in all—comprise what is referred to as The Royal Family. An estimated 2,000 of these progeny constitute the "inner circle" of the Royal Family.

Religion

When Muhammad bin Saud achieved power in the 1770s, he forged a strategic alliance with Muhammad ibn Al Wahhab, a conservative Muslim scholar ("ibn" is another Arabic term referencing birth history). Al Wahhab imposed a conservative version of Islam—Wahhabism—that continues to exist today.

Al Saud leveraged this relationship with Al Wahhab to position the Royal Family as the protectors of the "one true religion." The centers of the Islamic universe are mosques at the two holy cities Mecca and Medina, and the partnership between Al Saud and Al Wahhab became so integral to the Al Saud Dynasty's power that the ruling leader assumed the title "King and Custodian of the Two Holy Mosques."

Shifting Sands

Over the course of the last several decades, the Royal Family's leadership profile has changed. Why? One reason is that Wahhabism is no longer the only popular practice of Islam; some Saudis follow less conservative versions of the religion. Which form of Islam is the "true" form and which the Al Saud Dynasty supports are complex questions with varying answers.

A second reason for changes in the leadership profile is that the Al Saud Dynasty has, in the views of many, become unpredictable in applying Islam to justify decision making. On occasion, leaders take a "liberal" or "conservative" view to support a particular agenda item.

Perhaps another threat to the Al Saud Dynasty's power currently is its struggles to address successfully the nation's economic woes. Demographic and economic information in Saudi Arabia is difficult to confirm, but according to some studies conducted by international socioeconomic organizations it has been suggested that a significant number of Saudis under the age of thirty, and even a large number of the adults live in poverty.[1] To be sure, the King has deployed national initiatives to address job development and several are in active development.

Generations ago, when the Saudis lived in isolation, this failure may not have been as pronounced. But today, nearly forty percent of Saudi

---

1 Karen Elliott House, *On Saudi Arabia: Its People, Past, Religion, Fault Lines—and Future* (New York: Vintage, 2013).

youth and their families are active Internet and social media users (the highest percentage in the Islamic world); Saudi people understand that other countries, Islamic and not, live more prosperously than they do.

Black Gold

Al Rub Al Khali covers 250,000 square miles, a vast swath of land to the south and southeast of Riyadh, stretching to the borders of Yemen and Oman. Until 1938, that barren expanse largely was uninhabited except for Bedouin tribes. Then oil was discovered. Today, four of every ten barrels of oil produced in the world come from Saudi Arabia. While some of that oil is shipped to the U.S.—about twenty percent of the oil imported into the U.S. comes from Saudi Arabia—most Saudi oil exports are to India and other Asian countries. Oil wealth and Saudi Arabia's economy and culture are thoroughly intertwined.

Saudi Today...

Saudi Arabia occupies most of the Arab Peninsula. Some 27 million people live there, including 10 million non-citizens, many of whom comprise the country's working class. These visa workers, including Filipinos, Eritreans, Indians, Bangladeshis, Sudanese, Tunisians, and Pakistanis, are primarily employed as blue collar and domestic workers. Americans, Canadians, and Western Europeans also work in the Kingdom, holding positions in medical research, oil, and business.

For more than 700 years, native Saudi Arabians have organized into thirteen major tribes. Their strong identification within these tribes continues today, despite a recent mass migration to cities.

Five major cities in Saudi Arabia each house populations of more than one million, and nearly two dozen other cities boast 300,000 residents. Urban centers, connected by ultramodern multi-lane highways, tout skyscrapers designed by the world's most renowned architects.

...And Tomorrow

The world is watching Saudi Arabia. Issues such as the role of the Royal Family, the role of religion in the governance of the country, the laws and its legal system, banking, education, culture, the role of women—all these are vociferously debated and discussed, both in the Kingdom and all over the world. The future is marked with uncertainties and possibilities.

CHAPTER 5
Sunnis and Shi'a

Many Westerners (including myself, prior to living in Saudi Arabia) do not have a clear grasp of the differences between the two major sects of Islam, Sunni Muslims and Shi'a (or Shiite) Muslims. Here is this Westerner's understanding, based upon my own research and conversations with Saudis.

Saudi Arabia is overwhelmingly a Sunni state, both in its population and in its structures of governance and law.

The Source of Conflict: Succession

The conflict between Sunnis and Shi'as dates to the death of the Prophet Muhammad in 632 A.D. Some followers believed his successor, the caliph, should have been elected from among an inner group, similar to how the College of Cardinals elects a pope. Their recommendation was Abu Bakr, a friend of Muhammad. This group came to be called the Sunnis.

Others believed succession should be by bloodline, like royal lineage. Their choice was Ali bin Abu Talib, Muhammad's cousin (and son-in-law). The term Shi'a derives from "shiaat Ali" or the allies of Ali.

Abu Bakr triumphed and became caliph. The division between the two groups intensified and led to the murder of Ali's son, Hussein, by Sunni troops.

Sunni and Shi'a Muslims share the core belief that Allah is God and Muhammad is his messenger. Also, both groups follow the five pillars of Islam (in briefest outline: declaration of faith, daily prayer, charitable giving, ritual fasting, pilgrimage to Mecca).

However, the two groups evolved with different religious traditions and practice. Sunnis look to the Prophet and use his teachings for inspiration and direction. Shi'as put their faith in their leaders, called imams and ayatollahs; Shi'as believe these men are infallible because they are appointed by Allah.

Sunni and Shi'a Today

Today, Shi'as are the predominant Muslim population in several countries, including Azerbaijan, Bahrain, Iran, Lebanon, and parts of Iraq and Pakistan. Overall, however, Sunnis greatly outnumber Shi'as: Sunnis comprise about eighty-five percent of all Muslims. In particular, Saudi Arabia's Sunnis make up about ninety percent of the Kingdom's Muslim population.

CHAPTER 6
An Exploratory Trip

Six weeks after my videoconference, I watched Mary Ann smile and wave goodbye at Madison's Dane County airport.

That afternoon culminated a long process. The day after the videoconference, I picked up the phone in my office. I hesitated for a moment, a little incredulous at what I was about to do, then dialed Peggy Johnson. "Nothing ventured, nothing gained," I thought.

"Dr. Dolan!" she said, and I could almost hear her smile. She sounded genuinely pleased. "How are you today?"

"Very well, Peggy, thanks," I said, "I had to look around to find where I'd written down your number."

"That's right," she said. "I believe this is the first time you're calling me."

"It is, as you might've guessed, because I'm interested."

"Wonderful," she said.

"So what happens next?"

The next steps, I'm happy to say, involved leaving the itinerary and planning almost entirely to her. All I had to do was pack my suitcase.

"Your travel plans are all set," she said during our next call, just a few days later. "For the last leg you'll be Prince Sultan's guest on their national airline, Saudia."

"Well, I suppose that's where you'd find an airline called Saudia."

Peggy laughed (politely, I supposed). "The itinerary takes you from Madison to Chicago to London. From London, you'll fly onward to Riyadh."

In preparation of our call, I had printed information about Saudi Arabia from various websites. On the reverse side, I began scribbling the itinerary Peggy had supplied.

My passport was up to date and Peggy had taken care of my visa. Though I had acquired background about the country, I explained to Peggy, "I want to be respectful of the customs of other travelers and my hosts. Is there anything I should know?"

"Well," she replied. "Let's see. You already know alcohol most likely will not be served, right?"

"Mmm hmm. Not a problem," I replied.

"You'll be there for business meetings, but just in case…shorts are not considered appropriate, even though it does get quite hot. And men should keep jewelry to a minimum." I took careful notes. I knew about calls to prayer and the prohibition of alcohol and pork, but the thumbs-up comment was a heads-up to me. "Ah, yes, it's also considered impolite to show the soles of your shoes, so take care to point them downward while crossing and uncrossing legs during a seated conversation. Oh, and perhaps you already know that it's considered rude to touch a person with your left hand."

Peggy went on. "You may notice men are much more affectionate than here in the States. It's common to see men walking hand in hand or kissing cheeks." Hearing my pencil quickly scratching across paper in the background, she let a small laugh escape as she stopped advising and said with reassurance, "The Prince is *so* pleased you are coming and he knows you are new to the country. And, Mr. Naif will meet you at the airport and answer any questions you may have."

From what I had read, Riyadh was a sizeable city of five to six million people, holding most of the major government facilities as well as the primary residences of many members of the Royal Family. But, while those *primary* residences were in the Kingdom, many family members owned properties around the world: London, Paris, New York, Hong Kong, Montreux, St. Tropez. A far cry from a university employee's life in heartland America!

I also found out that the nation's original thirteen tribes still held strong allegiances for Saudis. The tribes predated the country-founding actions of Abdul Aziz in the early 1900s. As far as I could determine, marriages outside extended families and tribes were relatively rare, and a bloodline tended to stay within a given tribe. This practice had considerable implication for my work, seeming to support my very tentative hypothesis that the Saudi population, or at least these tribal subpopulations, were genetically alike—so much so that it could predispose them to inherited diseases.

But, real investigation was still many steps away.

The flight to London was perfectly uneventful. I had made the trip before, particularly for scientific conferences. But as I prepared to board my Saudia flight, I could feel an adrenaline jolt.

At the gate, I noticed that several male passengers assembled with me were dressed in gleaming floor-length tunics—thoubes—and with cords—igaals. Naturally, not every man on the plane was a Saudi, and plenty of passengers were wearing Western-style dress, but gentlemen wearing white thoubes was something I had never seen before.

Most of the women were wearing Western clothes, which skewed toward very conservative business attire, but a few were swathed entirely in jet black gowns, called *abayas*: capacious, tent-like thoubes and wraps that covered them head to toe, usually sans face covering. Some women, those I assumed were older, took it a step further and added black gloves and tiny mesh veils—*burqus*—over their eyes. I had seen women on the news dressed this way, but in real life it was astonishing to me. I wondered how much of this dress was voluntary and how much was imposed by society or their families. Or, for these women, perhaps it was business as usual and the voluntary/imposition issue never even crossed their minds. Though I was genuinely curious, I knew it would be grossly impolite to ask about members of the opposite gender. Perhaps I would get to know some people well enough to ask such questions.

In a wholly different vein, I was also struck—delighted!—to find I was flying first class. As I would come to learn, employees of the Royal Family often fly first or business class on trips, particularly the more senior members. It was my first time ever sitting "up front," and it was exquisite. I don't think I imagined the unspoken camaraderie, as though we were part of an exclusive club. Oh yeah, I could get used to this part of the work.

Settling in, I took note of the pilots and crew: the pilots a mix of American and Saudi men, the flight attendants women of African and Asian descent. This, I would come to see, was representative of the country as a whole; a neat microcosm, in fact. Nearly one-third of Saudi Arabia's population continue to be foreign workers.

As soon as we pushed back from the gate, and before the usual preflight announcements, the PA system played a recorded message, *"Allahu akbar! Allahu akbar! Allahu akbar!"* which my seatmate informed me meant "God is great" or "God is the greatest." I learned that "Allahu Akabar" is a supplication said often at the beginning of travel. I wasn't in Kansas (well, Madison) anymore.

My helpful neighbor was a middle-aged man who appeared to be American. "Well, it's hard to argue with that," I extended my hand in introduction. "Terry Dolan."

"Rex McAlister," he said, shaking. "You in *ahl*?" American, definitely. Texan, to be precise, if I recognized the twang. My mind processed his question: "You in oil?"

"No, you?"

"Yessir. Saudi Aramco. I'm an engineering manager." He paused as if that should speak for itself.

"At, I'm sorry, where?"

He laughed. "Oh, you're *not* in oil, are ya? Saudi Aramco's the Kingdom's state oil company. Best employer I ever had. They take care of your housing, and they sent my oldest to a fancy boarding school back home. On them."

I nodded, impressed.

Rex continued, "With bennies like that, most professionals headed to Saudi seem to be in oil, 'least in my experience. Lots of architects, too. I figure, you've got a country that was nothin' but sand sixty years ago. Now you've got five cities with more than a million people. Lots of building goin' on…and they don't skimp, let me tell you! Pretty little thing I was talking to at the gate said she recognized a few famous architects just on this flight.

"So," he finished, "what brings you to the Kingdom?"

This didn't feel like the time to name-drop a Prince I know only by videoconference. Besides, my professional integrity told me to keep my client's project to myself. Naif's words stuck in my head: *We wish to insist that these discussions remain confidential.*

"Just going to meet some colleagues," I said, then added, "I'm a neuroscientist."

Usually, almost always, the phrase *neuroscientist* instantly shuts down a line of inquiry. An emergency exit, if you will. It worked again. "Oh," said Rex with a nod, and returned to his in-flight magazine.

I was amazed by the graciousness and hospitality surrounding us. Flight attendants brought us fresh, cool fruit juices before we even took off. Shortly thereafter, they offered us dates—the best dates I've ever eaten—followed by a menu. Not your standard "chicken or fish" on Saudia. We had six choices of hors d'oeuvres, all of which involved caviar (not really my thing, but it was a nice touch), and four of entrees, all served on very fine, delicate china with actual silver utensils. I wondered how much of this was happening in coach.

"I think my wife would be impressed if I took her here for our anniversary," I volunteered to Rex. "Not necessarily Saudi Arabia. I mean the *plane*!"

"Sure would be nice to have a drink, though," Rex said. "But that's forbidden in Islam, you probably know. It's *haram,* they say."

As I began to take in just how far from home I really was, I regretted not having a farewell Dewar's at Heathrow after all. Instead, I made do with "Saudi champagne," a concoction of apple juice, grape juice, and seltzer water.

The flight was already an experience I'd never forget. It was about to become even more memorable.

While I was seated for the Saudia flight, awaiting take-off, one of the pilots, an American, came walking down the aisle. He and I began talking and during our conversation, I confided in him that today was a day of firsts and an extraordinary experience for me. He mentioned he would be on the "nap" shift at the beginning of the flight, but after a couple of hours, he would be flying the plane. If I was interested, I was welcome to join him in the cabin for a coffee. Needless to say, I was flabbergasted and enthusiastically accepted.

He was true to his word. Shortly after the first call to prayer, a flight attendant escorted me to the cabin. It was remarkable. The co-pilot was sitting back, sipping tea, and talking on a phone. The pilot monitored instruments as the autopilot guided us. As we entered Egyptian airspace, the sight was magnificent! The pilot pointed out landmarks, clearly visible at this height, many dating back to World Wars I and II. For a while the only visible landmarks were railroad beds, constructed by General Rommel during World War II. These rails appeared solitary, desolate, and displaced, crisscrossing in a desert vast as the eye could see.

Years later, with the heightened security after 9/11, I realized how rare and fortunate was my visit to the cabin.

Somewhere—I guessed we were over southern Europe—I noticed several Saudi men rising at about the same time and heading for the lavatory. And not coming back. Curiosity piqued, I made for the restroom to do some reconnaissance.

I entered, then abruptly stopped, surprised and a little wary. The place was soaked, with water splashed liberally around the floor and counters.

At that moment, the door to the neighboring lavatory opened and a Saudi man emerged, barefoot and carrying his shoes. I watched him walk to the rear of the aircraft, where I saw an area without seats. The lighting overhead was dimmed, and carpets were spread across the floor. The men were gathering back there, lining up their shoes and kneeling. They all faced the same direction. Periodically, they would touch their foreheads to the floor.

I hadn't been close to an Islamic religious rite before, and I admired the piety of the kneeling men. (Mary Ann and I are Catholic, and I tried to imagine having Mass on an airplane, and soon realized we probably wouldn't even attempt it.) I remembered that one requirement of Islam is prayer five times a day, facing Mecca, the holy city which happens to be in Saudi Arabia. A compass mounted on the wall was there to help the devout get their bearings. Touching one's forehead to the ground, I guessed (correctly, it turned out), was a way to submit before God. And the lavatory was wet because ablutions—washing hands, face, and feet (the last is problematic on an airplane)—were required before prayer.

The flight was long enough that I witnessed two of those periods of prayer. No announcement was made; the men seemed to know when it was time.

As we approached Riyadh, it was the ladies' turn to move en masse to the lavatories. They emerged wearing veils and loose-fitting, ankle-length black gowns. "They're called abayas," said Rex, my self-designated tour guide. The women did not seem to be carrying their western clothes, so I guessed the new garments were covering their original clothes.

We locked our seat backs and tray tables, and the plane began its descent. I kept searching the window trying to pick out lights or shapes, but saw only a wall of blackness. If I had re-set my watch correctly, it was well past midnight Saudi time. We would approach and land in the dark. To my surprise I found it frustrating: here I was, further from home than

I had ever been (in every sense), descending toward land to begin a task I couldn't speak about. And, I literally couldn't see what I was getting myself into. It was not a comforting metaphor.

We landed. And despite my advance work, nothing prepared me for my first moments of arrival in Saudi Arabia.

The terminal was sparkling, immaculate. Incongruous to imagine it rising from the desert. Magical if not for the uniformed men armed with automatic weapons who were everywhere. What threat did they expect to disembark? Who were they trying to intimidate? It only took a moment for my answer.

Down an escalator was a cavernous room jam-packed with hundreds of people, organized in lines. I could have been mistaken, but they seemed to be organized in separate queues by country: Filipinos, their belongings packed into soft-sided sacks; Ethiopians, draped in loose fabrics; Pakistanis, dressed in *shalwar kameez* and plastic sandals. They shared a look of exhaustion; also in common was the look of their tattered, worn clothing. I saw no Westerners, no Saudis, and certainly no Armani suits. Massive suitcases and sacks surrounding each traveler suggested theirs were one-way tickets, and these were all their worldly possessions. It troubled me that so many used their bags as pillows and mattresses. They had been here for hours...or longer. At the head of each line was a booth, likely for checking visas and papers. Not one booth was occupied.

For the sake of accuracy, I should note two things: first, the apparent grouping of persons by nationality, I learned, was the reflection of the fact that each line was the result of which flight they had arrived on. Ethiopians had arrived on a flight from Ethiopia, etc. Secondly, the apparent organization by country was subsequently not-so-apparent in subsequently visits. I remain ignorant as to the organizational strategies by which incoming expatriates are now processed.

As I navigated the terminal, with wayfinding signs solely in Arabic, I wasn't sure where to go. I figured...hoped...it wasn't into that human warehouse, but felt a little queasy all the same. I decided to keep an eye on Rex who was in front of me, and follow him until someone told me otherwise. "Betchya you're glad not to be down there, huh?" Rex asked, jauntily, turning around in front of me as he walked. "Saudis consider these folks to be from servant countries. They're domestics, basically. I hear they're paid squat and don't get much more than room and board. And, a lot of the time, their employer takes their passport." The last observation took a moment to sink in. "*Takes* their passport? And keeps it? Isn't that illegal?"

Rex laughed and tilted his head toward a soldier, clad in olive-green fatigues and carrying an assault rifle. "Illegal? Tell it to these guys."

"But that sounds like slavery," I protested. "Why do they come here?"

"Cuz it's even worse for them back home," Rex replied. "Least they can *get* work here. A little pay is more than none, and most of it goes back to their own country."

I looked out into the mass of humanity below me, already demeaned and belittled before they'd even cleared customs. Some welcome. Rex laughed. "Not everyone gets served a steak by a pretty Chinese stewardess."

"She was Malaysian," I said, distractedly.

As our line neared the escalator my mind was racing, trying to determine where I was supposed to go. Was there an American line? How did this work? Before panic had a chance to set in, I heard, "Dr. Dolan? Over here."

Not sure I've ever been so relieved to hear my name spoken by a familiar voice. I looked to my right and there, in a gleaming white thoube, was Naif. He was taller and more slender than I expected from our videoconference. As I approached, he spoke in Arabic to two armed men standing nearby, and with soldierly precision they stepped apart, opening the way into a glass-lined hallway, peaceful and absent other passengers. Naif shook my hand and, together, we turned down the passage.

"You've got some fine colleagues, there, Dr. Dolan," I heard Rex call out behind me with a chuckle. "Treat 'em good; they'll treat you good."

The passage led to another open space, its ambiance the complete opposite of the other waiting room. It was like a cathedral, hushed, with marble covering every surface, even the ceiling. As we chatted quietly and formally about my flight, Naif escorted me through the space, fancier than any government building or church I'd seen in Wisconsin, into a secluded reception area bedecked with opulent furniture.

"Please make yourself comfortable," Naif said. "My assistants are processing your paperwork and luggage."

"Do I need to do anything for that? Do you need my identification?"

"Not at all. Please, relax."

Royal treatment, indeed!

A white-thoubed attendant, a teenager no more than fifteen years old, suddenly appeared at my side. "Would you care for tea or coffee, sir?"

"Ahh, tea, please, thank you," I said, thinking of the hundreds, possibly thousands of travelers just five minutes away who might be stuck in that terminal, no food or drink in sight, through this night and into the next day.

After roughly half an hour, another aide came in to speak to Naif, who rose and announced, "Right this way. Our driver is waiting."

"And my bags?"

"Please, let us take care of it."

As we left the reception area and walked toward a set of doors, I noticed it was dark out.

Two a.m. or not, my first breath of outdoor Saudi air hit me like a blast from an oven door. Even on a July day at high noon back home, I can't say I ever felt anything like it. It had to be upwards of one hundred degrees. Dry heat or not, it was sweltering!

Welcome to the desert, I thought.

Fortunately, our ride waiting at the curb was air-conditioned: a black Toyota Land Cruiser. This one seemed to sit lower than those I had seen before, and as I stepped in and tapped on the window, the black-tinted glass made a heavy thud. Another first: my first ride in what seemed an armored vehicle.

"We will take you directly to your hotel," Naif explained, sliding into the back seat next to me. "At 8 a.m., a driver will pick you up and bring you to your meeting with Prince Sultan." Less than six hours of sleep? So much for the life of luxury! But to be honest, my nerves were still so a-jangle that I couldn't imagine sleeping at all.

Even in the middle of the night, Riyadh knows how to make a first impression. During the drive through what I took to be the central business district, we passed countless shops offering the biggest names in *haute couture:* Versace, Dior, and more. As chauffeured SUVs idled at curbs, groups of women in black abayas drifted through doorways into gusts of AC. Windows displayed luxe dresses; Oscar red carpet–worthy, to be sure. I noticed they were arranged on hangers, not draped across mannequins.

"Naif," I said, "is there any reason I don't see mannequins?"

"Mannequins?" he repeated. "Oh, of course. Depictions of the human body are haram. They are against Islam. But it is a practice that is changing and mannequins may soon be used commonly."

"I see," I replied, imagining just how much this included. Anatomical drawings for medical students? X-rays? Statues honoring heroes, etc.?

Women swished back out into the night with shopping bags full, I figured, of those gowns. And that's when it struck me: some of these women might be spending—who knows how much—on exquisite dresses that wouldn't be worn in public; only with immediate family or among other women. I wondered if, on this street at least, abayas concealed Fifth Avenue-caliber apparel. Later in my stay in the Kingdom, I would learn that my first impression of Saudi shopping was skewed. As in most countries, women had an array of options, from those high-end stores I saw to lower-end stores with mass-produced goods. Not everyone can or does spend thousands on fancy formalwear. I also learned subsequently that typical department store hours of this type close at about 11 p.m. but are open later (e.g., 2 a.m.) during periods such as Ramadan.

We swept past skyscrapers, thirty stories or taller, and finally pulled up in front of my hotel...a Holiday Inn! It proved to be the nicest Holiday Inn I'd ever seen. Perhaps the nicest hotel, period. The chain obviously accommodated to the Saudi market, and if the shops I had seen a few blocks away were an indication, that strategy made sense.

Once in my room, I immediately called Mary Ann.

"Hi there!" I said. "I made it!"

She sounded delighted. "Well, you certainly sound chipper," she said. "Are you having a good time?"

I thought of the private reception I'd received, and the crowds of immigrants who, unlike me, would be spending the night on the floor of the airport. "A good time... hmmm...that doesn't really quite sum it all up," I said, "It's a complex place so far and definitely an experience!"

"What time is it there?" she asked.

"Just after 2 a.m. How about there?"

She laughed. "Cocktail hour, honey. You're nine hours ahead."

I glanced out the windows at glowing, bustling Riyadh. "Well, aren't we the jet-setting pair," I said.

CHAPTER 7
A Prince among Men

Excitement and nerves jangled me awake before the alarm could. Just a few hours after hanging up with Mary Ann, I opened the shades and looked out in amazement at Riyadh by day. This was not what I had envisioned! I had imagined Lawrence's Arabia on wind-swept and desolate dunes, but this was L.A.! The view from my Holiday Inn window was an eight-lane highway, congested with bumper-to-bumper traffic, and a forest of skyscrapers. Yet, I felt soothed by the urban thrum. It was familiar. From eight stories up, this new world felt reassuringly small. My nerves subsided. I felt confident and ready for what the day would bring.

The first thing the day brought was eggs. Ah, the indulgence of room service breakfast! I was able to order my standard Western omelet with nonstandard, tasty *beef* bacon. Thousands of miles from home, with not enough sleep, little things count.

At 8 sharp, I stepped out of the elevator into the lobby and found not only Naif, but also a familiar figure in Western dress.

"Good morning," William Cornish said, cheerfully. "How was your flight?"

"Well," I said, "it wasn't short, but it was sweet! An academic from Wisconsin is happy for first class, I can tell you that."

Naif led us to our ride, another Land Cruiser. It occurred to me that as a senior aide, Naif probably had coordinated every single detail, all the logistics for this trip personally, and was responsible for ensuring all went smoothly now. Trust me when I tell you, Midwestern scientists don't usually enjoy this level of service, and I was appreciating every moment.

I noticed that Cornish, as I did, wore a jacket and tie in spite of the heat. Heat that felt even *more* intense than the night before.

I'm generally a warm-weather fan. Mary Ann, the person in our home who turns down the thermostat and opens windows, would have a lot of adjusting to do.

Perhaps because we were in the heart of Riyadh, the street level view of the city looked even more like Los Angeles than it had from my hotel window. We drove down broad boulevards with palm trees gracing the medians and lining the streets. Sidewalks were ample too. *I guess they're not hard up for space here,* I thought. These gracious sidewalks led up to office buildings and boutiques that would have been at home in Midtown Manhattan.

As we drove, the buildings became smaller and less ornate, beige in color—close to Pantone Sand—and with less form-over-function glass than we had passed before. Individual offices gave way to high-walled compounds, with blank street façades. On some of the facades, a small brass plaque by the entrance gate offered the name of the organization housed within, often in English as well as Arabic. If the area surrounding my Holiday Inn was where Riyadh went to play and shop, this was where it went to work.

After about a fifteen-minute drive, we turned into the driveway of a walled compound. The plaque read "Diplomatic Quarter." A long line of ten or twelve cars waited for a security and paperwork check from armed guards before they could enter. As at the airport, we were singled out for special treatment. Our driver slipped into an empty lane labeled "Pass," briefly conversed with a guard, and was waved through.

"As you'll have noticed," Cornish said, "we're entering Riyadh's Diplomatic Quarter. This is where many foreign embassies and consulates are; it's also where a lot of diplomats and other non-Saudis live."

I thought that showing me my prospective neighborhood might be a bit premature, but Naif headed it off. "If you do choose to come work with us here you'll have the option of living in the Quarter, but we have come here to meet Prince Sultan."

As we wound our way through the Diplomatic Quarter, I silently tried to guess where that meeting would take place. The Quarter was full of attractive, clean, contemporary buildings. The architecture, the landscape, the lush greenery—just the feel of the place evoked a suburban tract of Anywhere, USA. Comfortable, friendly, approachable. Maybe that was the idea. One thing I didn't see in "Anytown" though: foreign flags hoisted outside. I also noticed a number of unmarked commercial buildings, some with signs in Arabic and some with no signs at all. "Are there Saudi government facilities here as well?" I asked.

"Some are, yes," said Naif. A moment later, the SUV pulled alongside a large building. A two-story subsection of it bore a sign: Prince Salman Center for Disability Research.

"Is this it?" I asked both men. I was familiar with international disability research, and had investigated even more before my trip, but I had never come across the PSCDR.

"This is our stop," Cornish said, "but I should let Prince Sultan do the explaining."

We stepped out, crossed a small and blazing-hot forecourt, and entered a reception area where we were evidently expected. Roughly a dozen people formed a prim, respectful line across the lobby, waiting silently. All but one, a Saudi, wore Western business attire, minus coats and ties. The non-Saudis I assumed were clerical or support personnel, and all were men. Since I had left the hotel, even when I was *at* the hotel, I hadn't seen one woman.

The Saudi was the first to speak. He stepped out from the line as we entered, extended his hand, and introduced himself as Ghazi Al Shalon, "Welcome to the Center."

"Dr. Dolan," he continued, taking the same relentlessly poised and formal tone as Naif did. "His Highness will be along shortly. In the meantime, would you kindly accompany me upstairs?"

Al Shalon led our small group—Cornish, Naif, and me—up to the second story and into a conference room. If I can call it that. This was like no research center conference room I had ever seen: grand, and decorated with no thought to expense. The furniture was French provincial; the conference table, which could seat thirty or thirty-five, a gleaming expanse of polished cherry, Hagiographic portraits of Saudi men, all flatteringly lit, all around middle age (or *my* age, which, I was coming to accept, wasn't really middle age anymore), lined the walls. Most had weathered faces, commanding stares, and formidable, somewhat out-of-date mustaches. "These are the former kings," Cornish said quietly, when he saw me surveying them. Taking note of us again, Al Shalon beckoned me to a seat next to a particularly regal chair which, I assumed, would be occupied by the Prince. I sat. No one else had taken the cue; Al Shalon,

Cornish, and Naif were still standing. I sat, awkwardly, on the edge of the cushion, wondering if I should still be standing, if I had committed some sort of *faux pas*. Then an attendant appeared, seemingly by magic, at my elbow. He held a brass coffee urn with an improbably long swan neck. His other hand held an improbably small white cup. No one asked me if I wanted coffee; the attendant just started pouring, straightening his arm to increase the distance between the pitcher and the demitasse as he poured. Suddenly, he cut off the pour, the coffee stopping just shy of the rim. He hadn't spilled a drop, and throughout, his face had remained impassive, even absent. At my research center back home coffee service is not quite so ceremonious—it is dispensed into a paper cup, from a vending machine, down the hall.

Show-off, I thought.

The coffee itself was even more of a surprise. It was so odd, I thought at first something might have gone wrong with it. A sip barely passed my lips and I tried to suppress a grimace. Perhaps unsuccessfully.

"Arabic coffee is mixed with cardamom," Naif explained. "It is not to your liking?"

"Oh, no, it's...it's very nice," I said, and gamely took another sip.

"Very good," Naif said, to Cornish and Al Shalon. "Let us wait outside." And without further explanation, the three withdrew to a small room we had passed.

I waited. Alone but for the coffee pourer. And waited some more. With each moment, I became more anxious, anticipating that the next few minutes could well determine the direction of my life. I had nothing to do but think. And sip my weird-tasting coffee. Each time I would empty my little cup, he would immediately come over and refill it. I was not enjoying this coffee. I was nervous. And I had no idea how to say "no thank you." As if stolen from a Samuel Beckett play or maybe the animated *Fantasia*, all manners of negatively-intended sign languages were for naught, the coffee just kept coming.

Later, when I had become a friend and associate to the Prince I relayed the story of the never-ending coffee. After laughing delightedly, he told me of another occasion when a visiting American had simply, in desperation, slipped the cup into his pocket to halt the ceaseless refills.

So, yes, there I was with my tiny "bottomless" cup of bitter coffee under stern faces of men who had ruled the Kingdom of Saudi Arabia. I surveyed them with interest. These were kings. Real kings, not like in a parliamentary democracy, but with real power. These men ruled by fiat and marshalled significant force. Their expressions did not convey beneficence; in fact, they appeared as commanders who knew their power was not derived from the consent of the governed and guarded by mutual respect for the law, but by their familial might alone. I heard a rustle of activity from outside the conference room. *At last!* Through the open door, I watched as my three hosts, joined by the Center's staff, jostled to shake hands with someone I felt sure was the Prince. From the scrum emerged a handsome, regal man in his late forties. At six feet tall and draped in a cream-colored thoube, he was quite distinguished. Even his head covering was like none I had seen: several feet long and threaded with glittering threads.

Behind him trailed an entourage of eight or so men, all Saudi, who must have arrived with him. Respectfully, I rose, crossed the room, and extended my hand.

"Dr. Dolan," Prince Sultan said, with genuine kindness, clasping my hand in both of his. "Warmest welcome to my country."

"Thank you very much," I said. "It's an honor to meet you..." I paused; the words actually felt funny coming out of my mouth, as if I were in a movie, "...Your Highness."

I was struck by the Prince's easy confidence and earnest charm. I would later learn just how incredibly down-to-earth he was: the kind of person who remembers everyone he meets, and when he next shakes their hand, he greets them by name.

A few more pleasantries, and we moved toward our seats. I waited for the Prince to take his seat and then I followed, as did the others. "Allow me to present to you my companions," said the Prince, gesturing toward his entourage.

One by one, he identified each member of the group. Each was a cousin to Prince Sultan, and I was reminded that the Prince likely had *hundreds* of cousins. Some of these men were heads of what sounded like moderate-sized government departments. They all gave their names, too, but after the first two I gave up trying to write them phonetically on my legal pad. Perhaps "Your Highness" would serve for each?

The introductions finished, a brief silence fell as everyone respectfully waited for the Prince to speak. He began: "Please accept my sincere thanks for agreeing to come to our homeland. We have gathered here for a discussion of great importance to the Kingdom of Saudi Arabia and to the future well-being of our nation. The momentousness of the issues we are going to discuss cannot be overstated. I am deeply concerned about health issues in my country, and as a prince it is incumbent on me to take responsibility for bringing my people the aid they require."

I was won over by the Prince's charm and graciousness. He was literally princely. I was struck, too, by his heartfelt tone. Sure, we would have to see the data, but the Prince knew something, and that something genuinely worried him. The concern he felt for his subjects was authentic.

As the Prince turned to his entourage, he continued to speak in formal and elegant English. I assumed he had been educated in the U.S. or Britain.

"Gentlemen," he said, "as we have discussed before, it is our responsibility to take a leadership role in combating the health problems that face our nation. To that end, we have invited an esteemed expert from the United States to discuss these problems and seek strategies to address them." I straightened a little in my seat. "That is the purpose of our meeting today. As you are also aware, it is our hope that these discussions evolve into specific strategies that will involve our eminent guest, Dr. Terrence Dolan."

The entourage nodded agreeably. This clearly was Prince Sultan's show.

"Our understanding of these problems is emerging," the Prince continued, speaking to me but including his entourage. "However, what the issues have in common is that they affect our children. Although we are not experts, we have studied these diseases sufficiently to understand where they may be coming from. Our belief is that our children are inheriting these diseases from their parents.

"This is why we have turned to you, Dr. Dolan." The entourage nodded to signal their inclusion in the royal "we." The search firm we retained for our investigation quickly identified you as an eminent leader and the director of one of the world's foremost centers on child development."

I nodded. There wasn't much point in being modest. Besides, it occurred to me that any confidence I showed could be contagious, which might be useful to my prospective employers.

"I do not hesitate to admit," Prince Sultan went on, "that we are eager to draw on your expertise over a term longer than this visit alone. We hope that you find the magnitude of our challenges compelling, and that you find the circumstances under which you would live and work here appealing."

He paused, which I took to be my cue.

Uncertain about the protocol for how much to say, I kept it concise. "Thank you, Your Highness, for your generous welcome and for all the hospitality you have already shown. I am eager to learn more about the specific health issues and particularly how I can be of service." *I was starting to get the hang of conversing with royalty.*

Prince Sultan nodded, then stood. As one, his entourage rose as well. I gathered myself to follow suit but he gestured downward "No Doctor, please." He began to circle the room, gesturing broadly.

"The Center where we are meeting today is a small, initial effort to address the infant and childhood diseases that are at issue here. It is a token of our commitment, a way to show you that we are serious about improving the health of the Kingdom's children." He paused, next to an ornate settee and in front of a window overlooking a tranquil courtyard lush with date palms.

"We wish to expand this facility into a national research center. We recognize that the present facility is not sufficient for the undertaking we are proposing. However, we are fully prepared to commit the resources required to develop an institute that, under your leadership, will be sufficient to address these vital issues."

The phrase "commit the resources required" rang in my ears. Music. On the surface, the Prince's words seemed innocuous, delivered with the mannered precision of a careful English student and the propriety of a man accustomed to a modern-day court life. His words sank in. He was offering something that virtually no scientist is offered: *carte blanche*.

I would get whatever I needed. Simple as that. In my world of scientific research, that simply never, ever happens. I was awestruck. Most researchers at my level haven't done a hands-on experiment in decades. We're tirelessly dedicated, to be sure, but the experimental work is done by grad students and postdoc fellows. Most often our work delves into the mystery and complexities of...funding! I spend a great deal of time writing grants. True, we teach and write and review papers; sometimes we even get to do the fun part of science, when our students and postdocs come to us with data and we puzzle through it together. But the money spigot must be constantly turned. Usually, funds come from the government, but there is never enough to fund every deserving experiment. Science, as a result, is almost permanently hand-to-mouth. It's a life of constant asking, constant hustling.

As the meeting wound down, there was one last interchange that I remember fondly and have reminded the Prince of on several subsequent occasions. Prince Sultan began the interchange by saying: "Dr. Dolan, let me make one final comment. I am most anxious to move my concerns forward. I am in my late 40s and am most probably at the half-way point in my life. On behalf of the people of my homeland, I believe this is a dramatically important issue and I'd hope to address it in a timely manner."

I realized this was a manner of terminating the discussion and required my final comments. I began by saying: "Prince Sultan, I'm most appreciative of your concerns. In fact, I just turned 60 and I believe that I am exactly one-half of the way through my longevity. And like you, I am looking forward to my next major endeavor. I thank you for your generosity and your commitment of support will be crucial, I'm sure, to whomever leads this effort, me or another capable researcher. Naturally, my involvement will depend on a number of issues that we'll need to discuss. Still, I'm extremely interested to learn more about this. The remainder of my time here will be important to our discussions and to what the future holds for me."

"I am glad to hear it," he said. "As you know, my esteemed associates and I are not scientists, but we share a growing and intense interest in these diseases. To continue to impress that upon you, this afternoon I would like you to meet two other colleagues who share my hopes. One meeting is with the Minister of Education and the other is with the Minister of Health. They would like the chance to meet you. I hope this is agreeable."

"Of course," I said. The efforts expended on me so far were certainly enough that I would accommodate their itinerary. "Where will I find them?"

"My assistant, Naif, will accompany you. We aim, of course, to make this trip as effortless for you as possible. We hope that will also make it effortless to say yes," he said smiling. "Mr. Cornish will accompany you as well. This evening, unfortunately, I'm not able to join you, but I invite you to have dinner with Mr. Cornish, who can give you a Westerner's perspective on living here. I hope you find it useful and convincing."

"Thank you," I replied, "although I'm sorry to hear you're otherwise engaged."

"Looking forward to it," said Cornish.

This certainly felt like home. Every academic job interview in my entire career, whether as interviewee or interviewer, had worked this way: the department chair kicks things off; you meet a couple of potential future colleagues to discuss the work that awaits you; an interesting person takes you to dinner and tells you what it's like to live and work there; then the boss again before you leave. The Prince, the Ministers, Cornish—this was textbook recruitment and I was pleased.

Not knowing what else to say, I thanked the Prince for his time.

"The pleasure is mine," said Prince Sultan, and rose. So did his entourage and this time, so did I. As we all shook hands, my mind toyed with the idea of having an entourage. Certainly there were advantages: strength in numbers, people to make things happen for you and smooth the path; but I could also see how it would get tedious for me. The Prince whirled out of the room, his associates trailing briskly behind.

Naif and Cornish remained behind with me. "Right this way," Naif said, and led us out. As we fell in, walking toward the door, Cornish asked, softly, "How're you holding up?"

The truth was I was overwhelmed, but I wasn't sure how straightforward to be, so I kept it neutral. "Well! Very well!"

"I remember what it was like when I first came here," he went on. "It's a lot to take in."

"So far, so good," I said, cheerily.

He nodded. "Sure. We'll talk later."

In front of the Holiday Inn at around eight that evening, I climbed into the passenger seat of a Jeep Wrangler, next to Cornish. I hadn't seen him since our morning meeting at the Center.

"No entourage?" I asked as Cornish started the truck.

He laughed. "Unlike the Al Sauds, the Cornishes don't usually travel en masse." He checked for traffic, then pulled away from the curb. "Please do call me Bill, by the way. May I call you Terrence?"

"Absolutely! Make it Terry."

Until this moment, each of my Saudi interactions had been formal, stiff. Casting off this layer of pomp was akin to unknotting my tie at the end of a long day. I relaxed into comfort and relief.

"Great, Terry," he said, cheerfully. "I think you'll find, *if* you should spend a significant amount of time here, it makes a real difference to have refuge from the formality and hierarchies, and the battalions of royal cousins that seem to be everywhere. The expat community here is a good bunch, but we can talk about that later. I'm sorry about the earlier snafu and missing your meetings this afternoon. How did it go with the Ministers?"

I paused, then laughed. "Kind of hard to tell apart, to be honest with you. I mean, in the meetings and discussions you wouldn't know which was Education and which was Health."

"I figured as much," said Cornish. Bill, I should say.

"I've got to admit, they were pretty uninformative conversations," I said. "It felt like they were checking a political box, more than anything."

"What *did* they say, if you don't mind my asking?"

"Not too much. They're pleased that Prince Sultan is taking this on; they're also pleased to meet me; they will be *so* pleased to offer me any assistance I might require. Which, of course, was of no assistance at all."

Bill said, "Because…"

"Because I have no idea what I could even ask for," I finished. "As I said, the meetings were just for show."

"Yeah, there's a bit of that here," Bill said.

"I imagine tomorrow will get a little more into the nitty-gritty," I speculated. "It'll be more substantive, I hope."

"That's the intent, I believe."

"And so will tonight!" I said. "It sounds like I have a lot to learn about life in Saudi Arabia."

Bill smiled. "I'll do what I can."

Watching the palm trees and tall buildings through my window, I asked, "So Bill, how did you come to know the Prince?"

"Well, I moved to the Kingdom nearly a decade ago to do organizational consulting. I met the Prince at that time, and began helping him with some planning projects. I like a dry heat," he chuckled, "and so here I am today."

"Well, I'm very happy he arranged for us to meet," I said.

"Yes, me too. I think he understood that I could give you a sense of the history of the PSCDR, and even more important, a North American perspective on living in the Kingdom, should you decide that's for you."

As we entered the dim, low-slung restaurant, it seemed at first that one of my hypotheses was incorrect. "Are there only men allowed in here, too?" I asked Bill, as we were led to our table. "I figured, if this is a place where expats are likely to be…"

"Behind there," Bill said, gesturing toward a wall that turned out to be a heavy wooden screen. As I attuned my ears, from the other side of the screen I could hear women's voices and boisterous children. "That's where all families sit, Western and non-Western."

The menu was familiar, not much different from any of the "Middle Eastern" (or, I suppose, specifically Lebanese) restaurants in Madison. After we had ordered shawarma and fruit juices, I got down to business.

"All right, Bill," I said. "I do have a lot of questions. It feels like there's no end to what I need to know, but if any questions are out of bounds, I hope you'll just say so."

"Don't worry. I doubt that'll be the case," he reassured me. "At the same time, some of what I say will be *just* my personal opinion. I'll be frank, but don't forget that it is just my opinion."

"Of course," I said.

"Great!" he said. "Fire away."

As we dove into a plate of pita with hummus—admittedly, quite a lot better than what I was used to back home—I started. "All right. This is less a question than a comment. It's what I alluded to earlier. I'm surprised at the lack of detail in every conversation I've had with officials so far."

Bill nodded. He was clearly expecting me to say precisely that.

I went on, "I figured that if they flew me halfway around the world, they would provide a certain level of specificity about the project, the parameters, the scope of the problem. To make my being here worthwhile for them, if nothing else. We only have a few days, after all. I'm leaving tomorrow night."

Bill was still nodding. He was obviously thoughtful, considering his response. "Yes," he said. "Yes, that's exactly right. Your comment hits on a central issue, probably *the* central issue, that the Royal Family is up against today. Maybe I should give you some background, to clarify why they're in such a precarious position."

I imagined the Prince, his entourage, his wealth and power. "Ahh, I'm sorry, a precarious position? Prince Sultan?" I asked, incredulously. "What do you mean?"

"Let me start with a little background," he continued. "I'm not sure if you've had a chance to look much into the history of the Kingdom?" He phrased it as a question.

"Oh, just a little. I certainly wouldn't call myself an expert." That would've been my answer anyway. Scientists are taught, either by their mentors or by failure, to be modest about what they know. But I definitely *wasn't* an expert.

"Well, then you might know that Abdul Aziz bin Al Saud, the...warlord, I guess you'd say, the father of the country..."

"Literally, it sounds like."

Bill chuckled. "Yes, you *have* done your reading. Well, the issue is that he didn't establish a representative government; he established a monarchy. In this case, it meant the entire country and all its land was owned by the Royal Family. In 1902, that didn't mean too much.

"Once they found oil, though, it turned out they owned a *lot*. And your average Saudi isn't blind to that. This is the twenty-first century."

I jumped in, "Not a century that has been kind to autocrats."

"That's true. And who knows when that might come home to roost in the Middle East. But it's not quite the same here, at least not in Saudi. My sense, and this is only my impression, is that the Saudis by and large don't *want* a democracy. That sounds strange for born-and-bred North Americans, I suppose." I remembered he was Canadian. "But their view of the system is a little less rosy than ours. From their perspective, citizens in democracies don't have a lot of real power. They've ceded it to anyone with political connections or money or both.

"The Saudis, I think, would much rather have a benign overlord: a father figure, a supporter. As you might've noticed, what they need to work on most is the 'benign' part. The penalty for thievery is to have a hand cut off. The preferred method of capital punishment is beheading.

"Oh, goodness, I'm sorry," he said, interrupting himself awkwardly. "This isn't suitable dinner conversation at all."

"Don't worry," I reassured him. "I've seen too many sick kids in my day to be squeamish about anything." And I already knew about the beheadings.

"Anyway," he continued. "Saudi Arabia now has a tremendous concentration of wealth, guarded ferociously and with extreme violence by the whole apparatus of state control. Meanwhile, frankly, the average Saudi isn't doing that well. Forty percent of the population lives in poverty. Don't ask me what we had to go through to get *that* information. And further, if information like that becomes public, people with power in this country are going to get antsy."

"I'm not sure I see how this translates to the superficial content in my meetings today with the Ministers."

"Right. The problem is that not everyone in Saudi is on board. They don't want to acknowledge there's a serious health problem here, and certainly not one that justifies the intervention of Western science."

I took a guess. "The 'not everyone' would be the conservatives? The Wahhabis?"

"Bingo," Bill said. "For a long, long time, Saudis have taken it for granted that their government, their society, their very lives were governed by Wahhabi dictates. But more recently, over the past few decades, maybe, the Wahhabis, at least, aren't so sure anymore. Today, Wahhabism is not the *only* type of Islam on the peninsula. More moderate forms have been gaining ground. Some conservatives are beginning to worry that not everyone believes the Wahhabi way is the one 'true' Islam. What's worse, the Wahhabis think the monarchy has started turning its back on them. Muhammad bin Saud, more than 225 years previous, was pretty blatant in using Islam to justify his rule, but either the royals are getting more honest about their motives or people are becoming more savvy about the philosophies and decisions really guiding the country. Regardless, Prince Sultan and his allies don't always fall in line to the clerics' satisfaction.

"And that's just the tip of the iceberg. Some Wahhabis are beginning to write about it, suggesting that the real enemies are not the infidels, meaning people like you and me, but the Royals themselves. "Got it," I said. "On one hand, a lot of people are realizing it's not the seventh century anymore. On the other hand, a few people are determined to hold back time."

"Westerners think all Saudi Arabians are wealthy. But put together these two facts: some seventy percent of Saudis are under age thirty, and a substantial number of them are unemployed. It's never a good sign when large numbers of poor, unemployed young men see no way out in a tightly regulated society. Some of the young are modern. Some are Wahhabi. And the Royal Family is stuck in the middle. No matter which direction they move, they make enemies. And they may be making enemies just by standing still."

"Damned if they do and damned if they don't. That's terrifying," I said. "But that may explain why the Ministers today were vague and noncommittal. Is it because they were trying to play it safe? They didn't want to say anything that would insult the Prince? If they wholeheartedly embrace this program they'll appear to be too pro-Western and rile the Wahhabis?"

"Yeah, that's what I think," replied Bill, shaking his head.

Our shawarma arrived, and as we started to eat he continued. "You know, I've heard estimates that the amount of oil wealth the family has invested in the U.S. stock market is between ten and twelve trillion dollars! That's what they stand to lose if there is a major rift between the East and the West. That's a heck of a lot."

I had to laugh at that. "Well, I sure don't have that problem!"

"Tell me about it," he said. "Anyway, Terry, you see where this is going. The Kingdom isn't collapsing, but that doesn't mean it's stable. And right in the middle of the Kingdom's health issues are the two of us. We represent the West. We represent infidel influences. We are trying to improve the country, or corrupt it, depending on which side is talking about it."

"I don't have any desire to get into all that. It's not my business," I objected.

"Me neither, but that's how people are going to see it, regardless of your intentions or mine. We represent modern science."

"And yet," I added "Avicenna, one of the first real physicians, the one who wrote the textbook every European doctor used till the Renaissance, was an Arab and a Muslim. In Baghdad, I think."

"True, but don't forget this," said Bill. "You represent a Westerner interfering in Islam."

"That sure is a dramatic way to put it," I said.

"People get mad about these things, Terry," he said, softly. "We have to be careful.

"And...," he paused. "At the risk of riling you up even more, my American friend, we can't take the moral high ground. The uncomfortable marriage of government and religion is not solely an Islamic condition. Even in the United States, there's a growing sentiment that it's acceptable, even desirable, to merge religion and law, or at least to blur the line between them."

I nodded in agreement. "You're absolutely right." In fact, just recently a political candidate in the United States said his religion and politics are one and the same. "I'm a churchgoing man, Bill, but this is, indeed, a slippery slope."

Bill leaned back and took a big gulp of pineapple juice. "Look, Terry, I hope I haven't overstepped here." He smiled, put down his glass and then in a more boisterous voice, announced, "I'm not trying to talk you out of coming! Not in the least. I would just feel dishonest if I didn't make sure you had the whole picture."

"I appreciate that," I said. "It's just kind of infuriating, frankly. Science has done so much to relieve human suffering over the years. The world is healthier than it has ever been in the entire history of our species. Isn't it arrogant or short-sighted to refuse the benefits of science on behalf of other people?"

Bill had no answer. "It's an aggravating place sometimes, believe me."

I saw that this wasn't going to go any further. It's not as though I had to convince Bill of the merits of science, so I pushed on to another of my major queries. "I had another question. I've been to the Center and two ministries and I have yet to see a woman working at either of them. Are there *no* female employees there?"

"I thought you might bring that up," Bill said. "This relates to what we were just talking about. Now, there *are* women who work side-by-side with men in some places. But you only see this in specialized environments where it's required, such as a hospital. Women work, and I'm not sure you realize what a leap that must've been for Saudi, but they're segregated from men."

"Unbelievable," I said, shaking my head. "Except I do believe it."

"I think it might be important to make a distinction here. This is just my understanding, but, as far as I know, there's nothing in the Qur'an or in the way Muhammad lived that would suggest that discrimination against women is appropriate. I believe the restrictions are a function of Wahhabism. In this country, as you might've noticed, women aren't even allowed to drive.

"And," he went on, "in court, a woman's vote counts for half of a man's vote. Women can't travel without their husband or a male relative, and need permission from a senior relative to leave the country." He saw the frustration on my face.

"Well, you get the idea. So, it won't come as a surprise that employing women is a hot-button issue in this country. That's why, at present, there are no female employees at the Prince Salman Center on Disability Research. Prince Sultan and the Royal Family are trying to manage a precarious balance between tradition and change, and hiring women might tip that balance."

I was infuriated but, as Bill guessed, not surprised.

"It's baby steps. This is the first modern research center in the Kingdom that addresses women's and children's health, and it's named after the Royal Family. It's already leaning West. Hiring women may be just too revolutionary for some people."

Some of the brightest minds I knew were women, not to mention that when addressing what could well be a maternal health issue, women may be the only people who were allowed to meet and establish trust and connections with mothers in this country. I thought of the women who profoundly impacted my career. I imagined how many babies and new mothers would have suffered if not for Mary Ann's tireless work as a neonatal nurse. The injustice felt most profound when I thought of my daughters: that opportunities here would be closed to them simply because of an X vs Y chromosome. Ridiculous. How could any father feel differently?

"Bill, I have to be upfront, before I go much further down this path... this could be a deal breaker. Prince Sultan asked me to take the lead in dealing with the health issues of children and, by extension, their mothers. Trying to do this without relying on any women would be absurd!

"Are women even permitted to see male doctors?" I asked

"They *can* see male doctors, but most do not. And when they do opt to see a male practitioner, a female nurse or family member might have to be there, too. Your point is well taken. I know these inequalities are very frustrating to you," Bill continued, reeling back into a conciliatory tone.

"Honestly, Bill. Maybe I should just go back tonight. Save us all a day's work tomorrow."

"OK, Terry," he said. "Look, you're right. You're absolutely, entirely correct. Honestly, the Prince probably feels the same way. Between the two of us, I'm not sure I could work for someone who didn't at least *possibly* agree with us on this. And he has a huge aspiration to do good for this country. It's a struggle."

He seemed to reflect for a moment. "I think you should mention this to him tomorrow. Perhaps present the reasons the project would *need* women for it to succeed. He already trusts you, you know, and he dearly wants to address this health issue. You may persuade him.

"Just keep this in mind with everything you do or consider doing here: don't let the great be the enemy of the good."

I left dinner enlightened and deflated, frustrated and excited. It had been quite an extraordinary discussion from several perspectives. Also, I was already beginning to anticipate the discussions I would have the next day. First, my meeting with Naif would be illuminating regarding the personal circumstances if we moved here—housing, salary, living circumstances for Mary Ann and me. But even more important, tomorrow's meeting with the Prince would determine if I thought I'd be able to do any good here at all.

"Well, I see *that* won't be an issue," I said with a heartfelt grin. I was sitting with Naif in a conference room at my hotel, the morning after my dinner with Bill Cornish. Naif had just slid a sheet of paper across the table face down. Flipping it over, I saw their salary offer.

"His Highness did not wish for so simple an issue to pose a moment's impediment," said Naif.

"If only everyone, my former bosses for example, saw this as a 'simple issue,'" I said, and smiled. Naif looked genuinely puzzled.

But that was far from the most shocking figure on that sheet. Below my personal salary offer were prospective funding levels for the project.

In the States, a typical high-performing lab may have a few separate research projects going at once. The annual budget for each project might be a few hundred thousand dollars, perhaps even a half-million dollars. The figure I saw on the sheet was for nearly 300 times that amount!

It seemed absurd, inconceivable. I wondered briefly about currency conversions but, no, that was very clearly 150 million U.S. dollars. What *couldn't* a researcher do with that kind of funding? But it was so unimaginable that it just couldn't sink in.

So, I ignored it for the moment and moved on. "So what's next on the agenda?" I asked.

"To confirm, Doctor. You find this offer satisfactory?"

Mary Ann would enjoy hearing about my admirably cucumber-cool composure in the face of a palpitation-worthy budget.

"Very good. The next topic is…housing. In Riyadh, our honored guests such as yourself have two options.

"One is to live in a compound populated by Westerners. The compounds are walled and their gates secured. Many who come to Saudi Arabia to work in private companies live in those compounds." I thought of Rex McAlister and imagined a Texan, raised on the wide-open plains, now coping with a fenced-in life. "Many Westerners prefer this living arrangement because they are free of some customs they may find constricting. For instance, women are not required to wear abayas and may drive."

"That sounds nice. Is there a disadvantage?" I asked.

"The disadvantage is they are on the other side of Riyadh. It is a thirty- to forty-minute drive if there is no traffic. And there is *always* traffic."

I might've smiled to myself a little. When there's traffic in Manhattan or Chicago's Loop, it makes sense. Small area, lots of people. But what was the deal in Riyadh? *I know you're not running out of desert,* I thought, recalling my flight and the vast, lightless emptiness before we touched the ground.

"So what's my other option?" I asked.

"You could also live right in the Diplomatic Quarter."

"The same one the Center is in?"

"The very same. You may even be able to walk to your office."

"Interesting. And who lives there?"

"Diplomats and government officials from all countries. It is quite an international neighborhood. Recently even some Saudis are moving into the DQ."

I liked the sound of that. After our children were born, Mary Ann and I hadn't traveled as much as we'd wanted to. Who does? And, I rather enjoyed the thought of all of these other countries coming to us.

"Also," Naif went on, "the villas there are nice: three bedrooms and baths, lovely gardens, and perhaps a swimming pool."

"The *villas*?" I asked. To my mind, Bond villains and Italian counts lived in villas. I had always been perfectly content with a house.

Naif didn't seem to notice. "Regardless of whether you choose to walk to the Center, the Prince will provide you and your wife with a private car and a driver."

"That sounds terrific," I said. I was gearing myself up for the inevitable sticker shock. Finally, I forced myself to ask, "Do you know what the cost of all of this would be?"

Naif hesitated. "To Prince Sultan?"

"Oh! No, I mean to me."

He cocked his head slightly. "There is none, of course."

I nodded approvingly, as if free housing and a chauffeured car were the least I would ever have expected. "Of course, of course," I muttered. "Just making sure."

With my close colleague and friend, Prince Sultan bin Salman.

CHAPTER 8
Where'd You Get Those Genes?
Genetic Inheritance 101

Before I describe my next meeting with the Prince, let me provide a brief primer on the science and terminology of genetic inheritance and consanguinity.

First, a definition of consanguinity is easier promised than given. Different countries use different criteria to define it. Literally, it means shared blood, or a blood relative. For now, let's just say that it's when close relatives have children.

A caveat about the following paragraphs. It is estimated that the core of what we know about science is doubling every six months. That means the following is inevitably incomplete. It's also simplified. So this will be an abbreviated Genetic Inheritance 101 course, not a 201, and certainly not post-graduate.

To understand the inborn-error health issues facing newborns in Saudi Arabia, it's important to understand human inheritance. Genetic information is passed from parents to their children by way of DNA. DNA determines every aspect of a human organism's development, including height, eye color, and hair color, as well as the development of proper functions of all parts of the body and control of much of our health and well-being.

You've seen DNA's double-helix structure; it contains twenty-three pairs of chromosomes. Those chromosomes are contained in every cell in the human body except the red blood cells. The DNA is organized into pairs of elements called "base pairs" and the precise arrangement of those pairings is critical to correct development.

The individual elements in the strands of DNA are organized into functional working groups called genes. In each cell, there are approximately three million base pairs of DNA, organized into 20,000 to 25,000 genes.

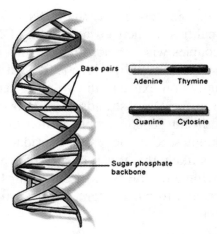

DNA's familiar "double helix" structure. (*Illustration from the U.S. National Library of Medicine.*)

If DNA is the genetic blueprint, then RNA is the process that helps carry out the instructions. One can think of the role of the DNA as producing an array of RNA, and RNA consequently guides the development of specific types of proteins.

Now, about those proteins. Proteins are large molecules made up of many amino acids and acylcarnitines (as' el carn' it eens), which transport fats into cells for energy and normal cellular processes. Our bodies are comprised of a myriad of proteins, each of which fills a critically important role. Proteins include antibodies, enzymes, messengers, and structural components; proteins can also provide services like transportation and storage.

From a genetic perspective, health and well-being are dependent upon the inheritance of properly arranged pairs of DNA, the subsequent correct production of RNA, and the final production of appropriate proteins.

To maximize the chance that the aforementioned production will occur gracefully and without aberration—in other words, to minimize the possibility of inborn errors—a proper and "normal" fertilization process is necessary.

That's where our parents come in. If two individuals procreate and their DNA interacts in a proper manner, all should be well (assuming no environmental or medical issues). Problems ensue if their DNA do not play nicely with one another.

Often, when first cousins procreate, their DNA do *not* play nicely. Why? First, commonalities in their corresponding DNA structures are more likely than in couples who are not first cousins. In fact, entire segments of their DNA strands could be identical. That type of overlap is extremely rare, virtually non-existent, in two unrelated individuals. Depending upon where in the DNA strands there is overlap, those anomalies may cause significant genetic problems that prevent proper RNA production, and—you guessed it—jeopardize production of the proteins required for health. It's likely that this sequence of events could result in an inborn error involving a disability or disease. Our first task would be to determine whether, and to what extent, inborn errors were affecting Saudi Arabian children.

CHAPTER 9
Children and Women

Arriving back in the Diplomatic Quarter, this time to the Prince's office, I read the sign out front: "Headquarters, Saudi Commission for Tourism and Antiquities (SCTA)." As I entered and waited in its rather Rococo parlor, I could hardly begin to imagine what "tourism and antiquities" could mean, or how this and the largest public health project in the country could both fall under one man's bailiwick.

I wasn't waiting long before a pair of dark, wooden double doors swung open and Prince Sultan glided out. (I was never sure if it was his regal bearing or his especially long, flowing thoubes, but he did always seem to glide.) He was thronged by a waiting group of Saudi men. Much hugging and cheek-kissing followed; when the crowd dispersed the Prince beckoned me toward his office, graciously smiling. As I approached, he extended his hand in a Western-style handshake. "Good afternoon," he said, warmly. "I hope you had a satisfactory time since we last spoke. Coffee." Not a question, it was an announcement that more cardamom coffee was on the way. *Great!*

I couldn't possibly decline. "That would be terrific."

As I headed into the office, I noticed impressive memorabilia on the walls and on credenzas, signed to the Prince from a who's who of scientific and political leaders. The most impressive (to me) and the most personal were written communications from President Ronald Reagan. (To remind the reader, Prince Sultan bin Salman is the first Arabian individual to ever go into space. On June 17, 1985, he was an Astronaut on Flight Discovery that spent just over seven days in space.)

As we sat, Prince Sultan launched into a brief speech. "I hope the past several days have helped you envision what your role here could be. As you know, I feel a certain responsibility, as a member of the Royal Family of this Kingdom, to be a caretaker for my people. I believe much good can be done to address these illnesses we have observed, and I am eager to begin." As he spoke, a coffee server poured silently at a side table between our chairs. *Here we go again with the coffee, I thought. This time my strategy would be a sip or two to be polite, then no more.* The server bowed and exited, and the Prince and I raised our coffees.

"So then, your discussions with Naif and Mr. Cornish, they have been satisfactory?"

"Very much so," I said. "And I appreciate the sincere intentions you bring to this project." I paused, still editing in my head what I was planning to say. I was nervous about being forthright about a sensitive issue, but I wasn't going to leave the country, let alone come back, without having a conversation with *some* substance about what I was supposed to do.

"Your Highness, allow me to be frank. I came to this particular meeting hoping that the two of us, between ourselves, could speak in a little more detail about what, precisely, you want to do."

Of course," he said. "In my view that is a question I am hoping you will help us answer." He lifted what looked to be an ostrich-skin folio from the side table and opened it on his lap. "My physicians and medical advisors inform me that we may have a high incidence of...Please, bear with me... lysozomal storage disorders, phen... phenyl... PKU[2]... and other diseases, and that their incidence may be growing."

"Understood."

The Prince continued, "I appreciate their skill and knowledge, but my medical advisors have nowhere near your level of expertise."

"So, to be clear about our objectives, we first need to determine how widespread these illnesses are. Secondly, we must determine their causes. And finally, we need a strategy to educate our citizens, treat these diseases, and eradicate them from the Kingdom."

No small feat.

---

2 PKU is the abbreviation for phenylketonuria. It is an amino acid disorder that occurs when the phenylalanine hydroxylase (PAH) enzyme is either missing or not working as it should. Each of us has a pair of genes that together make the PAH enzyme. In people with PKU, neither of the genes works as it should. They have inherited one non-working gene from each parent, and the result is they have difficulty breaking down phenylalanine, an amino acid, from foods and drinks they consume. The end result is a disorder that can lead to a variety of brain dysfunctions and, in some instances, result in death.

"Well," I hedged, moving unthinkingly into a mindset of scientific debate, "Currently, we have no way of knowing whether the incidence of the diseases you mentioned is abnormally high and growing in your country. If they are, we would want to address that immediately." I continued. "But in general, eradication of any disease is difficult. Even when a disease is environmental or where we can control the spread, eradication is a long-term program. And eliminating birth defects is much more complicated."

The Prince seemed tense, unmoving, the posture of a man receiving unwelcome news for which he hadn't been prepared.

"I don't understand."

"Well, there are many kinds of birth defects. Some are caused in utero: by things that happen to the mother while she's carrying the child. Fetal alcohol syndrome is one example. If a mother drinks too much while carrying her baby, the child may be born with mental defects." I paused, then said softly, "This is probably not a problem in Saudi Arabia."

"No, it is not."

"Another example may be if a woman carrying a child takes medication that affects the fetus. This is *not* a genetic problem. The baby has normal genes and was fine until the mother took the medication. These types of problems occur because mother and child temporarily share a bloodstream. Because they are caused by the actions of individual people, these problems generally are preventable. They may also be caused by environmental factors: exposure during pregnancy to severe air pollution or lead, for instance. In these cases, too, there may be treatments available to avoid subsequent birth defects.

"But there are other kinds of defects that are inherited," I continued, "defects that are caused by a gene the parents carry. Are you familiar with what I mean when I talk about genes and proteins?"

"Yes," Prince Sultan said briskly. "I have been briefed."

"Excellent," I said. "So you know that everyone has two copies of every gene, one from each parent. For some diseases, one normal copy of the gene—that is, from one parent—may be enough to prevent the disease, even if one parent gives the child a form of the gene that causes the disease. The baby may have half the normal amount of protein, but in some cases that's enough.

"But," I went on, "if each parent supplies a bad copy, the child will have the disease."

"I have heard this. I understand," the Prince said, and seemed to mean it.

"In instances like these, widespread genetic testing would be required to determine who has these genes. In fact, if what you wish is truly to *eradicate* the disease, the testing would have to be universal."

"Of course," the Prince said, unconcernedly.

Universal testing wouldn't be the hard part? I thought in amazement, trying to envision what that would entail in the U.S. *What a country this is!*

"Finally," I went on, "there is another group of inherited diseases, what we call *spontaneous mutations*. These occur when the parents have normal genes, but genes in one gamete—a gamete is the joined sperm and egg cells, the embryo—are damaged. This could happen as a random error while DNA was being copied over for that cell, or the cell itself could be damaged after replication by, say, radiation.

"The problem," I concluded, "is that these types of problems, spontaneous mutations, can *always* happen. They're random. They're completely unpredictable. So, while eradication is an admirable goal, it will be important to remember to be humble about what science is able to accomplish."

The Prince was palpably displeased.

I brightened. "Your Highness, I mention all of these things not to detract from the task at hand, or what you may accomplish by pursuing it. It's just important to set reasonable expectations."

The Prince nodded somberly. "We must always be accepting of the will of Allah, this is true."

With the science lesson over, it was time for more specifics. "Now," I went on, "let's say that the Kingdom *does* have a problem of this nature. Here is my question for you: if I come to Saudi Arabia, and we determine that this issue exists, are you of a mind to support me in forming a team and then resource it appropriately? This is a substantial task. The work will be national in scale and, I expect, a large number of institutions and agencies would be involved."

"I think I appreciate the enormity of the task," said the Prince. "It is what motivated me to seek out expertise of your caliber. To be frank, my family and I have little choice. The well-being of our people is at stake. *Our people*," he paused for emphasis, and it worked. His next words were deeply felt, *"They need your help."*

By this point, I already felt that I could hardly decline. But I tried to see the situation coolly. The Prince still wanted me to be part of this more than I did, and that gave me leverage over a huge issue, one that could be a deal breaker. It had been enough to keep my enthusiasm tempered.

"I'm grateful for your confidence," I said. "May we discuss a few issues that are on my mind?"

"Please," said the Prince.

"Thank you. The first issue, in all candor, the primary issue, is the role of women in this project. I have been told that, perhaps for good reasons, you're hesitant to allow women to be hired. However, to be perfectly transparent, I could not participate in this project if I were unable to work with women."

The Prince nodded, patiently listening.

I continued, "I say this for two reasons. First, for much of the work in maternal and neonatal health centers, it is *necessary to* focus on women and children. The people we will interact with, the people we'll need to persuade, the people, frankly, whose help we'll need, will be the *women of Saudi Arabia.*"

The Prince looked open, attentive. I thought he was doing a pretty good job for someone raised in a culture that, as far as I could tell, was not accustomed to admitting that it needed women for much of anything.

"From experience I know that in dealing with maternal health issues, mothers connect better and listen better to women staff members. Women staff not only bring medical expertise, but they also bring an important perspective, an understanding, and often an incredible devotion.

"The second reason is a personal conviction, your Highness," I said. "I cannot discriminate, or participate in discrimination, against a group of people solely on the basis of their gender." I was about to go perhaps a sentence too far, feeling myself fired up as I'd been talking to Bill the night before, and noticeably emboldened. I took a breath. "Your Highness, I understand I'm a guest in your country, but this is an accommodation I'm simply not willing or able to make."

It was difficult to stop there, to let several seconds of silence hang in the air after so strong a statement. *Yes, Mary Ann, I actually said that to The Prince,* I thought.

Then the Prince responded. He had been sitting back in his chair, lounging even, with his legs crossed. As he spoke, he uncrossed his legs and leaned in, lowering his voice.

"I know, Dr. Dolan," he said. "Mr. Cornish and I spoke earlier about your conversation last night." Inside, I winced a little. Partly because Cornish stole some thunder from my impassioned speech, and also because I started to replay in my mind everything I said to him the night before. I realized that he must have repeated some of it, perhaps all, to the Prince.

I refocused on the here and now. "You may realize," he went on, "that this is a difficult, complex issue in Saudi society at the present moment. I myself represent that complexity: I am a Prince of the Kingdom, yet I was educated in the United States, in an environment where men and women worked side by side, and very well at that. I hope you realize I feel nothing but respect and admiration for women." He smiled. "My own mother was one."

I laughed politely.

"At this point," he said, "I don't think it is appropriate for me to make an official comment on women in our workplace. However, I have had time to consider the issue, thanks to Mr. Cornish, and I hope you'll be pleased to know that I have developed a compromise."

A diplomat and a statesman, the Prince was a superb negotiator. I recalled the initial deal I had struck with Peggy to find out more about the project. Undoubtedly he had smoothed that process, as well.

"You may have noticed a fair amount of empty space in the Prince Salman Center for Disability Research. In fact, the PSCDR is quite a bit larger than it needs to be at present because I am assuming it will grow. For instance, the building has an entire second wing that is currently unoccupied. You may designate this as the women's wing.

"Professor Dolan, the issue, you see, is not *hiring* women, it is in having them work side by side with men. No workspace can include both genders. However, segregated workspaces are perfectly permissible in our society. Do you find this agreeable?"

I suspected the second wing never was intended as part of the Center, but that wasn't really relevant. What mattered was that the Prince had, in no more than a few hours, created a path around my primary objection before I could even voice it to him. His tenacious and creative problem solving was powerful testimony to how much he wanted me to come work for his people. I was flattered and I was moved by his concern for his countrymen…and women.

"I think that's an excellent idea, Your Highness," I said. But I was thinking ahead to situations when men and women might need to work together. "Would it be acceptable to designate one space that we'd use on specific occasions, for specific reasons that *require* men and women to interact? For example, when I organize a research effort of this scale, I form a group called a Program Advisory Committee to offer me input and guidance. Such a committee would need to include both women and men, and I'd want to meet with them every week."

"Let's…" the Prince began, then paused and smiled. Perhaps at my tenacity. "Let's do that. We'll work out the details when the time comes, but in principle, yes, I agree."

"Thank you. That is good enough for me," I said.

"Very good. Did you have other issues to discuss?"

I did. I needed to negotiate a start date. The University had a fairly flexible policy on sabbaticals but I needed six months to finish the term and get my affairs in order. It went without saying that I needed Mary Ann's concurrence as well. We tentatively agreed to an initial twenty-four-month project, beginning in six months.

The Prince seemed pleased, but hardly surprised. I knew I was dealing with a man used to getting what he wanted, and much experienced in doing what he had to do to get it. "This is excellent news, Professor. For me, and especially for the Kingdom."

"I'm glad," I said, and shifted gears back to business for a moment. I wanted to make sure we had clarity before I left. "So during the next six months I'll be starting preliminary work on this project. To give you an idea of what the preparations will involve, I'll develop a research plan, both short- and long-term, and consider how I can assemble both a research team and a support team, beyond the clerical staff already here. Of course, only so much of this can be done from the U.S. Will I be able to count on Mr. Cornish's help?"

"You certainly can," said the Prince, "and I will also ensure that whatever support services you need are available when you need them. The 'Saudi Commission for Tourism and Antiquities,' he gestured around him, "should have the personnel you require."

And then, for the first time, and with a deeply felt tone, he touched his heart and said, "Thank you. I am grateful, and Saudi Arabia is grateful."

"I appreciate that, Your Highness," I said, "but please...I haven't even done anything yet!"

CHAPTER 10
Should I Stay or Should I Go?

I'm sure I could have calculated exactly how long it would take to travel from Riyadh to Madison, including time changes. But the upcoming trip felt infinite, and I was too tired to do the math. I was already exhausted when I arrived at the Riyadh King Khalid International Airport departure lounge. The last forty-eight hours had been a whirlwind of jet lag, cultural immersion, negotiation, hidden agendas, and, let us not forget, bitter coffee. But it was all with the end goal of solving a daunting medical issue...for a prince! A prince I already admired greatly. Or maybe the fatigue was because some bureaucrat decided that 2:45 a.m. was the perfect departure time for an international flight: all flights from Riyadh to the west seem to depart between 1 and 3 a.m. These "unhappy" hours seem to me too early or too late.

Settling into my chair, I warmed to the realization that, after some phone calls, a videoconference, and a brief site-inspection, the Kingdom of Saudi Arabia was actively and urgently recruiting my help. I was flattered and a little bit daunted at the decision facing Mary Ann and me. So, though my body was weary, I rose, found myself a cup of coffee (Western style, this time!) and sat back down with a legal pad and pen. Across the top, I made two columns, *Positives* and *Negatives*.

It wasn't my first time with such a list. Some of my friends go on gut. They throw caution to the wind, dive in headfirst. I admire that, but as a scientist I'm not built that way. Throughout my life, practically every time I had a big choice—grad school, research topics, every job offer—I've wanted, no, *needed*, to see all the pros and cons in front of me. (No, Mary Ann, not that decision. And that one was unequivocally the best one of my life.)

The *Positives* came quickly:

Science! Saudi Arabia was a *natural experiment:* a laboratory that created itself. For neuroscientists, this was an opportunity of spectacular value. In heterogeneous places like the United States, it is difficult to correlate a particular disease with a particular gene. Too many genetic variations happen between any two people. Only a few places on Earth, Saudi Arabia one of them, are genetically homogeneous and isolated. At least in areas of the country where the incidence of marriage among first cousins was high, it might be easy to identify a gene for a particular disease.

I recalled a story I had been told, perhaps by one of the Ministers, about a family that had nineteen children, eleven of whom were afflicted with a similar type of deafness. In that situation it could be just a matter of months to identify the responsible genetic mechanism!

I was already envisioning the laboratory we could build: a world leader in genetics research, a site for paradigm-shifting discoveries surrounded by the sands of the desert. It was still hard to imagine myself staying in Saudi Arabia long enough to lead an institution like that, but I was thrilled to imagine helping it get off the ground.

Next: $$$! Funding also ensured this project would be far from the norm, especially from the way science is practiced today in the States. Back home, the National Institutes of Health, which funds a large majority of scientific research nationwide, has cut back from approving twenty to twenty-five percent of proposals a decade ago to about ten percent or less now.

Universities do not usually fully fund their research labs; the labs primarily depend on the NIH. So losing NIH funding is like going out of business. I personally knew scientists who had spent five or seven years after college earning a Ph.D., followed by years of low-paid postdoctoral fellowships and an agonizingly slow ascent up the ranks of science, only to have it all disappear because funding was stripped. Years away from family, years of missing one's children grow up, and decades of eschewing tempting salaries from private industry often are for naught.

I thought of a good friend from my early postdoctoral days, an incredibly diligent and clever neuroscientist, who discovered and published robustly, but whose funding simply ran out. His postdocs and grad students dispersed to other labs, his equipment was sold to pay the lab's creditors, and ultimately, he found himself in a low-ranking job outside of his field.

We scientists often feel like politicians, fundraising for the next campaign. Sadly, this role is as important as discovering and sharing the workings of the natural world. In recent years, as the U.S. has fallen into a deeper and deeper financial hole, the funding quest has become a losing battle.

Imagining that for a few years, that problem would not exist was something I simply couldn't ignore. I could focus again on the science of science! And my problem wasn't just solved, it was SOLVED! Financial support was a significant investment and vote of confidence from the Prince.

I saved the most compelling *Positive* for last. Doing good. If this project was successful, and one must be guardedly optimistic, it could help an entire country, and potentially even the world. Great achievements, I knew, depend on tackling great problems.

Allow me a moment of nostalgia. I was a young man in 1969, when Neil Armstrong walked on the moon. It was one of the greatest and most memorable moments of my life, watching something happen that hundreds of generations of mankind dismissed as impossible, the stuff of myths and legend. Tracking down genetic diseases was no moonshot, but it would probably save more lives.

And I'd be remiss if I didn't admit that, at my age, there was something immensely appealing, even irresistible, about gathering my strength one more time to take my own little moonshot...to dare greatly. I thought of a poem by Tennyson, "Ulysses," that I had read as a young man, and knew even then that it was something I'd return to in my later years. In the poem, Tennyson imagines Ulysses, or Odysseus, home from his ten years of fighting in Troy and ten more years of wandering the oceans with his crew. He's home, but the truth is, he misses the seas of Scylla and Charybdis and the Cyclops, he misses the sirens, and he wants one more adventure while he still has strength to take it.

"My mariners," he says, *"you and I are old; old age hath yet his honor and his toil; death closes all, but something ere the end, some work of noble note, may yet be done."*

Mary Ann and I had spent years focused on our children and our careers. It had been a long time since we had taken a risk, started a new path together. We both were adventurers at heart, people who seize the day, and what an opportunity this could be! I was excited about embarking on this remarkable journey together, sharing this experience whatever the outcome.

Dutifully, I turned to the *Negatives.*

It was Saudi Arabia. The cushy existence we would enjoy troubled my conscience, made me feel as though I would be supporting a system unfair at best, cruel at worst. I remembered Naif waving me through security while hundreds of Filipinos, Eritreans, and Pakistanis slept protectively and uncomfortably on their bags. Also, what I had heard of the criminal justice system seemed wantonly cruel and founded on negligible individual rights.

Women. Even though I felt confident the Prince would do the best he could to ameliorate sexism within our project, the country's overall attitude struck me as medieval, perhaps even malicious. I could hear the voice of my youngest daughter...*Is it right to respect others' cultures, even when they're repressive and unjust?* And as unsettling as Saudi Arabia's treatment of women was to me, I knew it would upset and directly impact Mary Ann even more.

My hand and eyelids grew heavy and I rested my pen on my pad. I reminded myself that these positives and negatives were based on a brief two days in the Kingdom. My impressions, though important, were cursory and premature. I still had a lot to learn, a lot to consider.

Hours (days? eons?) later, arriving in Madison, I saw the town through the eyes of a stranger. It was summer, and young men and women strolled in cutoff shorts and short sleeves. In outdoor cafes, they drank beer and took turns posing for and posting photos. They didn't have a lot of money. As students, many likely subsisted on ramen and pizza. I had known several who regularly sold their own plasma to pay tuition or rent. But there was a carefree ease here that seemed absent in Riyadh, even among the wealthiest residents. I realized that the differences between Madison and Riyadh loomed large just under the specifics of my *Positives* and *Negatives.*

After regaling Mary Ann with my adventures, I brought out my lists.

"So we're settled, then?" Mary Ann asked. I'd expected a little more apprehension, but she was smiling. She was excited about this, too. I laughed. At times like this I drew so much confidence from her.

Aside from my forty-eight-hour immersion, our knowledge about Saudi Arabia was based upon cursory tidbits of news and rumors heard at social events. When the subject of Saudi Arabia comes up here in the States, one of several topics arises: terrorism, religious wars, the subjugation of women, prohibitions against alcohol and pork, or limited educational facilities. Mary Ann and I both understood, even with this superficial understanding, that living in Saudi Arabia could be dangerous or difficult.

I talked to Mary Ann about my professional concerns as well: how the mission fit into the overall cultural environment and about the efforts of the Royal Family to improve the quality of life and health in the Kingdom. "The Prince is one hundred percent dedicated to me leading an effort to develop programs and strategies to improve the health of babies and children, and for their parents and families, but Saudi Arabia is not like the rest of the world."

I told her about the meetings with some of the Ministers and my conversation with Bill about the perception of Westerners. "Even if we managed to figure out what's causing these health issues, even if we could solve them and save countless lives, some in the conservative sector would see our presence there as an invasion into their society and culture. They feel they can care for their young on their own, without condescending advice from 'infidels.' Not everyone is going to be happy we're there. To some, we are ill-informed outsiders suggesting they change who they *marry, how they raise their kids.*"

"And how often did you feel unsafe when you were there?" she asked. "Oh, never. I...oh." I paused. "That was different, though. They arranged my accommodations and chauffeured me around. I was accompanied and escorted the entire time."

She nodded, "But we'd be living with other expats or in the Diplomatic Quarter? And, we'd have a driver, too, right?" I nodded. "Tell me more about the medical issue. Do you know more now than you did?"

With excitement, I explained how this particular project, this particular country, could provide a unique scientific laboratory. "Most Saudi Arabians still maintain a close relationship to the lineage of their original tribes. Most marriages are arranged within those tribes. In some parts of the country, up to fifty or sixty percent of marriages—sometimes even higher—are among first cousins. From what I understand, this has been the practice dating back centuries."

Mary Ann jumped in. "So you're saying that the gene pool is pretty homogeneous within each tribe. Even now. So the causes of early childhood diseases are probably due to genetic, not environmental, factors."

"Well, that's my tentative hypothesis. We'll learn more when we start doing genetic testing," I replied, noticing that I had used the word "when" and not "if."[3]

With Mary Ann's enthusiasm, I was feeling resolved. There were lots of little decisions to make, but the big one was pretty much made. We'd go!

But I had to be sure Mary Ann was truly with me on this. "Mary Ann," I said. "Knowing you support this means so much to me. You are such an optimist, but I don't know what will happen when we get there. There could be upheaval, there could be difficulties, especially for you. I'll be immersed in work, which for all its differences, will be familiar territory for me. I'm not sure how isolated you will be. It may be awful as a Western woman in Saudi Arabia. It could be dangerous."

And providing me with reason number one million and one on why I adore Mary Ann, she replied, "C'mon Dolan, we raised four kids. How hard could this be?"

Mary Ann and I make a great team, and by the end of the evening, we had a week-by-week plan for how we were going to pull off the logistics of this move. It was far from the first time we'd been faced with a task like this—after all, as young academicians we'd moved about every five years as we developed our professional careers, but there was a level of challenge here that kept us on our toes. Besides, we were well past the point in our lives when six months felt like a luxurious amount of prep time.

Our first decision was that I would handle the professional aspects of the move, such as arranging my leave of absence. Mary Ann would handle the daily life and household. My formal request didn't take more than half an hour, but the ramifications for my lab and my staff would eventually take many weeks to sort through. I had to arrange to have my Principal Investigator status on our grants transferred to a colleague, as well as make sure, on the narrow operational level, everything was set up to run smoothly in my absence. "But not too smoothly," I told the colleague who was taking the reins from me. "I don't want to come back, greeted by 'gee, two years *already*?'" Mary Ann, in the meantime, had to manage

---

3 Several years later after we'd been in the Kingdom for a considerable amount of time, that original hypothesis was shown to be mostly correct. The "mostly" refers to the fact that inheritance is not the only cause of infant and childhood diseases. Saudi Arabia is a rural and desert country, and it has numerous environmental issues, such as high levels of lead, that can be detrimental to human development.

everything related to our house, our insurance, our health care, and our finances. Bless her. I got the better end of that deal.

Much of my planning dealt with how I would actually execute this project once we got to Riyadh. To some extent, this was second nature. It was part of the reason I was asked to do this. Broadly speaking, in order to determine whether an unusually large number of children were being born with genetic defects, we would start by screening as many newborns as possible. It's a simple concept that's cruelly, preposterously hard to execute with anything less than a sophisticated infrastructure. And I didn't have any staff yet. I came to realize that my most important task over the coming six months would be to assemble my *own* entourage!

Professionally speaking, I was still completely alone on this project. My most immediate goal was to find an associate on the ground in Saudi Arabia who could join the planning phase. Some of my core team had to be women, and as many as possible had to be bilingual in English and Arabic. (Apart from the common *Allahu akbar* and the expression of thanks, S*hukran,* I myself didn't come close to matching the last part of that description.)

To start my recruiting effort, I emailed a wide range of research colleagues, both in the U.S. and abroad, announcing that Mary Ann and I were moving to Saudi Arabia. (Imagine how surreal it was to write *that* email!) In the email I explained that I was in great need of recruiting some colleagues and staff to join me. I articulated my belief in the worth of the project and its great scientific promise. The compelling scientific merit of the project involved child developmental neuroscience. My initial goal was to find a scientist, either Ph.D. or M.D., in a relevant discipline, fluent in English and Arabic, and a woman. I prepared myself for a long wait while colleagues emailed colleagues who emailed colleagues. I was asking a lot, and I expected scant, if any, replies.

I turned to my other recruiting task: finding scientists already based in the Kingdom who might be interested in joining us at the Center. For this, I turned to Bill Cornish, asking by email if he had contacts who would be able to help us find the staff we needed.

The very next day, and a Sunday at that, I awoke to find a wonderful, unexpected email from a fellow neuroscientist on the faculty of Vanderbilt.

Dear Terrence,

Greetings from Nashville! I read with great interest your note in which you described your search for an associate in your exciting new endeavor, specifically a woman scientist who speaks both English and Arabic. I am happy to recommend a student here at Vanderbilt named Heidi Al Askary. She has not yet completed her degree, but is defending her dissertation next month in our Child and Language Development department. I believe, though I would have to confirm, that her father is Saudi and her mother is American, but I can confidently say that she is a high performer in our department. Her academic record is superb, and I am told she is excellent at organizing student programs as head of the Student Arabic Association.

I hope you are not put off by her still being in school. I believe she is someone who may meet your needs, and I hope this proves to be helpful!

Regards,
David

Ms. Al Askary's phone number from the Vanderbilt student directory followed David's signature.

I could not believe the serendipity. With delight at this lead, and real bacon on my plate, I heartily enjoyed breakfast with Mary Ann.

My first step was to check Heidi Al Askary's credentials. Thank goodness for the Internet. You can do all this on a Sunday morning still in your pajamas. Happily, all seemed A-OK.

As morning turned to afternoon, I took a seat at my sunny little desk and began to compose my thoughts on a legal pad. Always the scientist. I dialed Ms. Al Askary's phone number, thinking back to Peggy Johnson's first call to me. Though it was Sunday afternoon, not Monday morning, I truly hoped that Ms. Al Askary would think that opportunity was calling.

"Hello! This is Professor Terrence Dolan from the University of Wisconsin." I hated introducing myself with the title, but wanted her to realize quickly that I wasn't a total crank. "I am Head of the Waisman Center at the University of Wisconsin. Do you have a moment to talk?"

"Sure," she replied, a little guardedly. "About what, exactly?"

I explained that my colleague from her faculty had suggested I contact her. "I'm embarking on a new project and he recommended you very highly. It so happens I'm searching for someone with exactly your technical and academic credentials, preferably bilingual in English and Arabic. May I give you the details on this project?"

"OK, Professor," she said carefully, "but I'm not sure I can help you. I'm still finishing my degree; I don't defend till next month. And I honestly don't really know where I hope to go after."

"I completely understand, Ms. Al Askary. I was informed of this already, and I assure you I'm still interested in speaking to you about the work I'm going to be doing.

"Let me explain. I just came back from a trip to Saudi Arabia where I agreed to take on a project. A few months ago, I received a call precisely like this one. In fact, making this call feels like completing a circle. My call was from a recruiter, but honestly I didn't know if it was a prank, or a scam, or what, which I'm guessing may be what you're thinking right now, too."

She paused and I could hear her smile. "Well, the thought did occur to me!"

"Well, let me be up-front: everything I will tell you over the phone, I'll confirm with you in writing or you can verify it yourself very quickly online. The gist of it is that I've been asked by a member of the Royal Family to take on a study of birth defects in the Kingdom, potentially genetic ones, as well as other developmental disabilities."

"I see," she said, with a bit less trepidation. "May I ask, which member of the Royal Family?"

Naif had been explicit about one point on my drive back to the airport, to a degree that the Prince himself had not: while discretion was vital for my own good and for the project, they trusted my judgment as to what I could say, and to whom. Not to be cavalier, but a cosmopolitan, educated Saudi woman was someone to whom I immediately gave the proper clearance. "Prince Sultan bin Salman bin Abdul Aziz."

"Oh, I know who Prince Sultan is, of course. My father knows him personally, in fact."

"Well, great!" I said. "Because of the nature of the work, it's important that we're a little discreet at this stage."

"And so...what *is* the nature of the work?"

I gave her the three-minute rundown: the potential issue; the Prince's interest; the political stakeholders. "In sum, the Prince has asked me to come to Riyadh for a period of probably two years to set up and run the Center. This leaves me in a bit of a tough position as an outsider. I don't have a team I'm bringing with me; I need to build one from scratch. And probably the first person I need on that team is someone with the right scientific background and the right language skills. And if that someone is Saudi, even better."

This time she laughed aloud, "Professor, I'm afraid you haven't just found someone who's Saudi. What about the fact that I am a woman?"

"And that is actually the best!" I said. "This is a project in maternal and child health. It would be absurd for it to be managed and staffed entirely by men."

She laughed again. "Does Prince Sultan know who you're talking to?"

Her concern was well placed. I needed to be careful, since now I was speaking for the Prince, not just myself. "He's aware of my requirement that women be a vital part of the staff."

"OK," she said, still sounding amused; probably by what she took for a foreigner's idiocy. "And, you are asking me to come to the Center?"

"Well, at this stage, Ms. Al Askary, I'm hoping to pique your interest so we can talk further about the mutual fit." It was straight-from-the-manual HR-speak, but I'd done this enough that it rolled off my tongue. "What are you considering for your next move after you defend?"

"A few things," she said: "perhaps postdoc work here in my current lab or at another university. I wouldn't rule out staying in the States, also as a postdoc; I've been talking to a few principal investigators in the U.S. And, of course, it's possible I would go back to Riyadh to work. My parents are there."

"Your parents are Saudi, then?" I asked, trying to make sure the background facts all lined up.

"My father is Saudi. My mother is American. They met while he was in graduate school at St. Louis University."

"Great," I said. I hesitated before my next question. From my point of view, this conversation was equal parts recruiting interview and sales pitch. "And what exactly is it you're working on?"

She gave me her three minute pitch, her elevator presentation. Her dissertation centered on the development of speech and language skills in children. Pretty soon we fell into the natural rhythm of shop talk. She became less wary, more open and enthusiastic. It never ceased to amaze me how quickly these shared, esoteric interests broke down barriers and established trust and esteem in their place. Before long, I had seen for myself that Heidi (she was now Heidi; I was still Dr. Dolan) was bright, clear-thinking, and focused in her work. She had decided that I wasn't a con artist.

Quickly, it seemed, more than an hour went by. I was completely won over and said as much. In equal measure, I was amazed and relieved: proficient, Arabic-speaking, Saudi, woman, scientist in the right field—it was like finding a specialized needle in an academic haystack. This adventure seemed to be coalescing almost too perfectly. But I still had to convince her to come on board. "So let me ask you this: what can I do to get you interested in joining this project?"

We agreed that I'd provide her, in writing, some detail about the Center including its plans for development and financing. She also wanted to have a sense of her responsibilities, job title, and salary. I knew that none of this information would be hard to gather: my royal *carte blanche* meant I just had to decide what they would be.

Besides staffing, another major project was to find a suitable lab. You can't conduct a genetic study without a high-quality genetics lab to process blood samples and screen DNA. Plan A would have been for the wet lab to be in the PSCDR. (The term "wet lab" is a reference to the blood samples and supplies that pass through the lab.) But that was never a realistic possibility, not due to a lack of funds or technical skills, but rather a lack of time. Building a wet lab—think bio lab from school, but with professional-caliber cell culture hoods, lab-grade freezers, PCR machines for DNA sequencing—takes serious time. It would certainly take longer than six months. I had decided almost immediately that waiting for construction was not acceptable, and I had been wracking my brains for an alternative. If a wet lab Plan B didn't reveal itself soon, our whole operation would be imperiled.

With so many wheels in motion, I wasn't surprised by a Monday morning call from Bill Cornish. I was, however, surprised by what he had to say.

He was responding to my email about potential contacts, I presumed. I greeted him with a hearty, "Bill, my friend, how are you?"

His hesitant reply and careful phrasing clued me in that something was afoot, and that he wasn't entirely comfortable. I sat forward in my chair, elbows against my desk, phone gripped a little more tightly.

"Terry, I saw your email. Looks as though you are beginning to recruit your team, and uh, I'm curious. It would be useful to know something." He continued after a pause "Have you given much thought to whom you'll be hiring?"

"I did reach out to an excellent candidate yesterday, and if all goes well, she'll accept my offer. Aside from that it's still early in a long process," I told him. "At this point, I'm focusing mostly on management, which is to say, my immediate administrative staff. Why do you ask?"

Ignoring my question, he continued, "And where do you think this next layer down will be coming from?"

"Oh, any number of places, but the type of people I have in mind congregate at maybe a dozen or so centers in the U.S. and Europe." I thought about the question behind his question. "There isn't much to report yet, really, but I'm happy to keep Prince Sultan in the loop..."

"No, no, that's not the issue," Bill said, then paused again.

"But there is an issue," I pressed.

Finally, he conceded, "In a way. They're not *Saudis* is what you're saying."

"Oh! Is that it? Are there some kinds of quotas that the Prince has to..." I began, but stopped when I heard Bill chuckling.

"No, no, believe me, the Royal Family doesn't worry about things like quotas," he said. "It's more...well...there are political sensitivities, you understand."

In the Midwest, we don't refer to problems with a vague "there are," and we certainly don't use phrases like "political sensitivities." With extra affability, I said, "Out with it, Bill."

"Prince Sultan...is under some pressure," he said "from others in the Royal Family. It's not like they all stand together, you know. They're in a tough position and sometimes they disagree on how to handle it. You and I talked about this at dinner: the Royal Family is constantly caught between modernization and the Wahhabis."

"Who are kind of the exact opposite of modernization," I interjected.

"You could say that. And to maintain, or try to maintain balance, sometimes it seems like *every* decision the royals make is political. This is one: they feel they need to lessen their reliance on Western expertise, including science and technology."

Now I was more than a little bit baffled, especially in light of the colossal efforts Prince Sultan had made to lure me, as non-Saudi as they come, to spend two years in Riyadh giving him Western expertise. I replied a bit tersely, "Well, that's rough timing."

Bill immediately took a conciliatory tack. "Look...Terry...all this means is, there's a faction of the Royal Family who will be a little alarmed by your presence. By mine too, probably. That doesn't mean Prince Sultan has to listen to them, of course. But let's realize that he has another angel sitting on his other shoulder."

"Funny-looking angel," I muttered.

"The Royal Family's scared," Bill explained bluntly. "because the conservatives are. Every time the conservatives see a foreigner working for their own government, they see it as a step toward the west, deserting their true constituents. To them, every Western scientist has replaced a Saudi somewhere.

"Practically speaking, I don't think this changes too much. We'll just have to involve the Prince in our recruiting and hiring a bit more, and there's going to be some kind of cap on the number of Westerners we can hire. I do worry, though, that the cap will be completely subjective and may change unpredictably."

"Yeah," I said, "I worry about that too. And, Bill, I have to ask...Why am I hearing about this now?"

"Prince Sultan only just gave me some perspective on the situation and asked me to relay it to you. I'm assuming the other Ministers you spoke to mentioned the situation to other members of the family, and concern started to snowball. Someone must have mentioned to Sultan that it was going to cost them, from a publicity perspective, to bring you on board. Not to mention a full Western staff."

I sighed a little, exasperated. "Bill, I'm a scientist. I'm there to do science. I'm trying to help solve a potentially explosive health problem that is harming their children. Their future. I don't have the ability or the inclination to think about how I function as a symbol or a pawn. This is above my pay grade and I hope it always stays that way."

"I understand," he said.

"Just tell me what I need to do, OK? But remember, and feel free to pass this back up to the Prince, that this project becomes more difficult if

I can't put together the right team."

It deeply troubled me that our presence in the country might be unwelcome to some, perhaps even to some members of the Royal Family. I was even more concerned about possible ramifications beyond our hiring and staffing. I mean, who knows what was next, how far this would go? Would every experimental protocol require approval from a committee of cousins, too? Would they control our results, and "edit" the data to suit political expediencies of the moment? I had heard of that happening before.

I also became concerned once more about our own safety. Deep down I was confident we'd be fine, but how could I know?

I hesitated to share my frustration and worries with Mary Ann, but I owed her the truth about these troubling thoughts. "I can understand them wanting to hire more Saudis, absolutely," I explained to her. "What bothers me is the deep resistance to Westerners. I have to be honest: I don't know what this means for us being there."

"What do you mean?" she asked, genuinely curious. "Do you think we're in *danger?*" She went on, "We'll practically be living in a spaceship while we're there, won't we? I'm worried I won't be able to drive anywhere. I'm worried it'll be too hot and I won't be able to get a gin and tonic when I fancy one. I'm worried that the food will be lousy. But I am *not* worried about us coming home!"

I smiled, then squeezed her hand. "Then neither am I," I decided. "Not anymore!"

I spent several days stewing about the two most immediate and significant challenges to moving forward with the project: the lack of a wet lab facility, and the new obstacle of hiring a primarily Saudi team, hiring people whose qualifications and skills were unfamiliar to me. Solving these two problems became the first thought I had in the morning and the one that kept me from a restful sleep at night.

Sometimes when you stop thinking about something, the answer becomes obvious. Sometimes the best ideas come in the shower, driving to work, or speaking with your spouse.

Early one evening, just as the sun was starting to dip below the horizon, and as Mary Ann was preparing her special meatloaf, I sat in the dining room leafing through a packet of materials from Naif. They presented "how-to's" for an expat living in Saudi Arabia. The packet included immigration details, instruction about Saudi Arabian social norms and etiquette, suggestions for travel in the region, and notes about halal meat. As the savory meatloaf aroma filled the house, I was heartened to realize that Mary Ann's specialty included beef and veal, but no pork—I could still enjoy it in Riyadh! The packet also contained a map and a list of services such as healthcare, where to find groceries or petrol, cleaning, and other info. My eyes went back to healthcare. Healthcare.

Wait...healthcare!

Quickly, I flipped back to the section about the King Faisal Specialist Hospital and Research Center (KFSHRC), also in Riyadh, where residents go for medical care. From what I could gather, it was a world-class tertiary-care academic hospital. With held-in excitement, I reached for my laptop and tapped a few keys. Soon I was reading about the hospital's physical plant, staff, and technical facilities.

As Mary Ann and I sat down to dinner, I excitedly told her about the possibility of using the hospital's lab space to test our genetic samples. "So, I think I may have solved the wet lab problem! I was just looking through the materials Naif sent us, and the hospital, not our research center but the general hospital, has a lab!" I exclaimed. "Maybe we could use their space and equipment to analyze our samples. We would have zero ramp-up time or costs. And, it's only a five-minute drive from the Diplomatic Quarter!"

"That would be perfect!" she answered. "You'll have to call Bill and see if they can make it happen. Well, another problem solved." She smiled. "Now, we just need to figure out a way for you to address the Prince's need to hire more Saudis. Maybe..."

Mary Ann paused and looked up at me with a mischievous grin. I knew what she was thinking because the same thought, at the same time, occurred to me. Forty years of marriage, after all.

"The hospital," she began, "maybe..."

I finished the sentence: "...we could use their people."

"Dolan, we are a pair of geniuses!" she exclaimed, laughing.

A subsequent conversation with Bill confirmed that, indeed, using hospital staff for our project could work. In fact, Bill had been thinking along the same lines.

A few days later, Bill relayed the Prince's decision that, in principle, he supported the idea. I began drafting requests for equipment and manpower, making some general assumptions about the number of samples we'd be processing.

The particulars of the hospital and its staff were unknown to me, and I had concerns: Who was the director? What expertise did the staff have? Was there specialized research equipment in the physical plant? What about governance? The lab staff would be dually employed, so who would have authority for supervising them? I was able to find many answers by corresponding with the hospital's senior staff, and some of those answers were quite reassuring. For instance, I discovered that the Director of the Research Center was an esteemed M.D. and Ph.D. and was, I was not surprised to discover, a distant cousin of Prince Sultan. That relationship held promise that the hospital might even prioritize our research project.

My sleep that night was almost restful.

CHAPTER 11
Sizing up a Saudi Workforce

Employment, or more specifically unemployment, is a current focus of the Royal Family that is attracting great attention. It is a particularly complex issue with historical, economic, and educational complexities of the highest order.

Historically, profits from oil had trickled down to the populace as an abundant financial safety net. As a result, many young people found they had no need to work at all. However, over the course of decades, the safety net has dissipated: while the *per capita* GDP had been over $26,000 in the 1960s, it had fallen to $12,000 (in constant dollars) by 2006. More and more families' sons and daughters are being forced to go to work, but they scoff at the notion of taking a job once occupied by a foreigner.

Rather than accept jobs perceived to be beneath their dignity and for meager pay, many Saudis have opted to remain unemployed. According to government-provided statistics, the unemployed constitute twelve percent of the nation, thirty percent of the youth, and thirty-five percent of women.

True, many jobs held by foreigners are low paying. Stephen Hertzog of the London School of Economics recently has reported that only 400,000 of the four-million non-Saudi-held jobs in the private sector pay more than 3,000 SARs per month (Saudi Arabian riyals: an equivalent of $800).[4] Quite understandably, citizens of the Kingdom, young and old, find that salary level unacceptable. Long hours, poor benefits, and weak job protection are also disincentives.

From an educational perspective, while part of the problem may have to do with a national sense of entitlement, that explanation does not tell

---

4 Stephen Hertzog, *National Employment, Migration, and Education in the GCC,* (Ithaca, Cornell University Press, 2012).

the whole story. The nation's educational system may also be partly responsible for such high unemployment.

Each year, 100,000 students graduate from Saudi colleges, but their education is often poor preparation for modern-day future employment. At least in 2001 the basic curriculum was theoretical and mostly theologically based. Few math and science courses were offered, let alone medical courses. These limitations begin in younger grades: elementary and high school students are often ill prepared for a good university-based curriculum, hence university graduates are ill prepared for the modern job market.

Repeatedly, I came across some notable exceptions. One exception was a group of motivated, skilled, local workers: Saudi women. I can only hazard an educated guess as an explanation. Perhaps women were more motivated because work was one of only a few outside-the-home outlets for their creativity and ambition. Ironically, their hard work and diligence still leads to more humble professional positions than those available to men. Women are prohibited from supervising men and gender-integrated work environments are prohibited, so the opportunities available to women are more constrained.

In recent times the Royal Family, despite determinations against them by conservative religious factions, are involved in focused ventures to improve the labor market.[5] Two of those efforts are the Nitaqat and the Hafiz programs. Nitaqat promotes higher wages by giving employers benefits and incentives for paying more. The Hafiz program pays unemployed Saudis $533 per month while they are seeking employment. Job-seekers are facilitated further by a national computer-based registry that pairs them with potential employers. These programs also endeavor to limit the number of work visas provided to non-Saudis, and also restrict how long a visa worker may stay in the Kingdom. Another undertaking has integrated online, employment-oriented job training programs in association with American universities such as Harvard and MIT.

In addition, as Saudi policy makers continue to build their labor pool within the Kingdom, I believe three relatively new or recently developed educational institutions also are setting standards for excellence. The in-

---

5 A recent unofficial report noted that the Royal Family currently is making it possible for nearly 100,000 students to attend baccalaureate and post baccalaureate education programs in North America.

stitutions are King Abdul Aziz University of Minerals and Petroleum, King Abdullah University of Science and Technology (KAUST), and Princess Nourah University. All three are models for progressive, technical education.

King Abdul Aziz University of Minerals and Petroleum sits on the serene, Western-themed campus of Saudi Aramco in the Eastern Province. Saudi Aramco, originally an American company, was established around 1940 on the heels of Saudi Arabia's oil discovery. It was an enormously successful company, and in 1980 it was sold to the Saudis. Saudi Aramco erected an American-style city surrounded by a high wall. Located on the East coast of the Kingdom, it feels like California, replete with grassy boulevards, single-story bungalows, laundromats, a theater (at this writing, one of only three in all of Saudi Arabia), swimming pools, parks, even Little League baseball! Women can drive on campus. King Abdul Aziz University of Minerals and Petroleum was founded to develop a pipeline of engineers and scientists. The institution's goals are graduates who are educated to Western standards and who are comfortable in the culture of Saudi Aramco's American-style community. Fundamental to the university's success and reputation is its commitment to awarding scholarships to capable Saudi youth. Saudi Aramco also identifies the most promising students from throughout the Kingdom and awards them scholarships to study engineering and science at leading universities outside Saudi Arabia. In exchange for the scholarships, the students commit to return and apply their skills and talents in Saudi Arabia.

Another example of forward thinking supported by the Royal Family is a relatively new university in Jeddah on the Red Sea: King Abdullah University of Science and Technology (KAUST). It is a mixed-gender university that emphasizes sciences and engineering in its curriculum. Again, it is a university designed to give Saudi youth the employment skills that Saudi Arabia desperately needs to boost its economy. Newer than the college-support programs at Saudi Aramco, KAUST already has established a reputation for excellence.

Lastly, Princess Nourah Bint Abdulrahman University is a new school dedicated to the education of women. Its patron, Princess Nourah Bint Abdulrahman Al Saud (1875–1950) was a member of the House of Saud and the elder sister of King Abdulaziz. The University boasts a stellar reputation and has a rapidly-growing student body.

But these excellent universities do not have the capacity to serve the entire Kingdom and can reach only a fraction of the nation's qualified students. Additional programs will further the country's ability to forge a skilled and educated citizenry.

CHAPTER 12
A Surprise Call from Our Daughter

It was early fall, around two months before Mary Ann and I planned to leave for Saudi Arabia. My secretary informed me my youngest daughter, Meaghan, was on the phone.

Meaghan and I have always been close, but her calling me at work was unusual—in fact, I couldn't remember her doing so since she was very young.

Any father's head would have been filled with the million or so thoughts that raced through my own. And 900,000 of them were worrisome.

At the time, Meaghan was a sophomore at St. Thomas University in St. Paul, Minnesota. She hadn't yet declared a major, and soon would need to do so. She was still struggling with the direction her studies, her future career, might take.

I tried to keep my voice light. "Hi Meaghan, sweetie! Everything OK?"

"Oh, yes, everything is fine. Didn't mean to worry you. But I did want to talk to you about something." An intake of breath, followed by a rapid-fire, "I-want-to-take-Spring-semester-off," followed by a relieved exhalation.

My immediate reply was "Good gracious! Why?" I was proud that she was in the honors program, on the Dean's List, and on an academic scholarship. I was surprised and couldn't imagine her reasons for wanting to leave school.

"Dad, I want to come to Saudi Arabia with you and Mom."

"Why in the world would you want to do *that*?" I exclaimed, trying to imagine my spirited daughter in Saudi Arabia. "You'd have to cover. You won't be able to drive. There are many restrictions."

"I know Dad, but none of that matters. I want to experience life in a conservative Islamic country. I want to see what it's like for a young woman to live there. I want to know about Islam, and about Saudi Arabia's culture, and learn one-on-one how they view Americans. I've been thinking about this since you told us about going there. I'll never get a chance to do any of those things unless I do this with you."

My immediate response, unspoken, was mixed. I was both proud and flabbergasted. My daughter is an extremely intelligent and open-minded young woman, driven to learn about the world. She yearns to contribute to society in a productive way.

As I thought about it, her interest made more and more sense. As our youngest she often joined our travels and international projects, and I suspect she wanted in on this one, too. What's more, her small university may or may not have been the best fit for her interests and aspirations.

Really, her request was more than reasonable. In fact, it might be a wonderful experience for all three of us. I hesitated because Mary Ann and I hadn't yet moved there, and we didn't know if Meaghan's presence would complicate anything. My role there was complex enough and I didn't want to make it any more so.

"I see you've been considering this carefully and I've got to say, I'm leaning towards saying yes. I agree, it'd be a once-in-a-lifetime experience. Tell you what. Talk to Mom about it, see what she thinks. In the meantime, I'll check the legal and cultural details to make sure it's OK on those fronts. Why, don't we arrange to talk, all three of us together, in the next few days? If we all decide it's a good idea, maybe it'd be best if you gave us a few months to settle in and learn the ropes before you come over. Sound reasonable?"

"Dad, that's awesome! Thanks so much! I'm so excited just thinking about it! OK, I'll call Mom and we'll all talk soon."

Mary Ann and I spent that evening discussing Meaghan's request, and I have to admit the idea appealed to both of us.

The following evening the three of us devised a plan: assuming all went as we hoped, she would come over in March. By then we might be organized and settled, and we'd have at least a few weeks together before the summer heat.

In the meantime, I'd start her paperwork.

PART II

CHAPTER 13
The Coffee Server's Son, Part II

A *gainst all odds and obstacles, months of questions to friends,*
friends of friends, family, imams, even to a neighborhood fruit
vendor and a long ago school teacher, led at last to this destina-
tion…this moment.

On a dusty street, under a blistering midday Saudi sun, Ibrahim
clutches the hand of his wife, Fatima, who in turn clutches the hand
of their two-year-old child. With equal parts apprehension and hope,
they approach a doorway. A sign in Arabic reads "Child and Newborn
Screening Clinic."

They share a glance, offer a silent prayer to Allah, open the door, and
cross the threshold.

A cool, bright office hums with activity. Ibrahim is welcomed, handed
a clipboard and pen and asked to complete a series of written questions
while they wait. Fatima entertains their son with a book and a puzzle.

A friendly and efficient young woman in a powder blue medical jacket
asks a few questions about Aziz's symptoms. She also asks some family
history questions, and then leads the trio to an exam room deeper in the
office.

Ibrahim tries to mask his worry about the needle necessary to draw
blood. Noticing his furrowed brow, the young medical assistant assures
him it will take only a second, and that it will sting just a little bit. She
speaks with a confident, reassuring tone that soothes all three. To Ibra-
him's surprise, and to his son's amusement, the needle is used to draw
blood from Ibrahim, then other needles are used for his wife and son.
They are instructed to call in three days if they have a phone; if they do
not, they should return to the office at that time. Ibrahim knows that it
will be a long three days.

CHAPTER 14
A Warm (!) Saudi Welcome

❝Well, now, I think that's my cue," Mary Ann said, looking around us in the darkened airline cabin.

From the carry-on by her feet, she pulled out a plastic-wrapped package. It was a black abaya purchased from a specialty shop in New York City.

Although we were airborne, still an hour from Riyadh, the first-class cabin started to hum with activity. Women started to make their way to the lavatories to slip abayas over their Western wear, and Mary Ann didn't want to risk missing her moment. She had been to Europe with me before but this was not a visit as much as an immersion, and she didn't want to miss any part of it.

"Hmm," she said as she returned, swathed in the mystery-making black I had almost come to take for granted in Saudi Arabia.

"Hmm," I echoed. "Is that you?"

"*Salaam Alaykum,*" she said in greeting. Along with *Shukran* for thanks, it was the first Arabic we'd learned. We both chuckled.

"This actually isn't too bad," she went on. "Kind of no point to still wearing the dress, though, huh?" I could see that keeping a second layer of clothes underneath would contribute to excessive warmth.

"But the dress was such a hit in Heathrow," I reassured her.

"Honey, I think I'm looking at years of shorts and T-shirts," she said. "I didn't pack right at all."

Soon the lights came on and, as if by magic, a different set of passengers was revealed. Half of them were now concealed in black.

Flight attendants began circulating, distributing juice and hot towels, and before long we heard the engines throttle down and felt the plane dip into its descent.

It was just before 1 a.m., and below us Riyadh glowed in the black desert like a beacon at sea.

"Are you ready for this?" I asked Mary Ann, putting my hand on her black-muslined forearm.

"Let me see," she said smiling. "I don't have to land the plane. I don't have to start a research center. I'm told we'll have domestic help. Yes! I don't think I have a worry in the world."

As we touched down, I smiled. "Welcome to Saudi Arabia!"

"*Shukran,*" she replied.

Unlike my prior solo arrival, this time we hadn't even entered the airport when I saw Naif, Bill Cornish, and a few familiar PSCDR personnel at the end of the jetway. Mary Ann saw my expression and asked, "Wow, we have a welcoming committee. VIP treatment!"

Greetings from everyone were gracious and heartfelt. The men hugged, Saudi-style, and, of course, nodded respectfully at Mary Ann. Naif assumed the role of host, greeting us on behalf of the Prince and letting Mary Ann know what we could expect for the rest of the evening. He also introduced us to a Saudi man we didn't recognize, a Diplomatic Quarter representative. The PSCDR staff, despite our objections, took our carry-on bags and went to pick up our checked luggage.

We were led directly to the same VIP lounge I had seen the last time. As we entered, Mary Ann whispered, "I'm guessing this isn't the room where everyone sleeps on luggage."

"Oh, I think we missed that," I whispered back. "Not sure I was supposed to see it the first time."

As we sat, a young man approached with a coffee urn and a tray of petits fours. "Would you care for Arabic coffee?" Naif asked. "It is blended with cardamom."

Mary Ann and I looked at our watches. "Yes, please," we said. We'd been in transit for twenty-one hours, and the trip wasn't over yet.

Even in the middle of the night and with our VIP status, it took nearly an hour for our paperwork and luggage to clear customs, again, independently of us. My mind returned to the room of travelers sleeping on their luggage. I could only imagine how long it would take for them to gain long-term entry to this country. We followed Naif through the terminal and when we exited through a sliding glass door, the outside air whacked us like a hammer.

"Whoa!" Mary Ann gasped. It was April and had been in the fifties at midday when we left Madison.

"Yeah, it's been in the nineties here at night," Bill said, apologetically.

"Wow" said Mary Ann, "how long has it been like this?" "Oh, I guess about a hundred years!" replied Bill with a laugh.

We knew what to expect, of course, and I had already experienced it myself, but there's something shocking about being smacked in the face with oven-like heat in the middle of the night.

As we approached the curb, we saw we'd be traveling by convoy: *two* black Land Cruisers were waiting for us. Mary Ann, Bill, Naif, and I climbed into one, while the PSCDR personnel and our luggage rode in the other.

We pulled away and soon were on the highway, surprisingly crowded for two in the morning. A Toyota pickup buzzed past us. A camel sat in the bed, impassively, gazing out to the side.

"Do you think camels like that as much as dogs do?" I asked Mary Ann.

Bill turned around from the front seat. "I'll tell you, I have *never* seen a camel move that fast. Mostly they just stand in the middle of the road and look confused."

We finally slowed down, pulling into the driveway of a compound with high walls. A group of well-armed guards in khaki clustered around the gate at the end of the driveway. Near the gate, in English and Arabic, a sign read, "Diplomatic Quarter."

"Almost home, I think," I said to Mary Ann.

After a brief conversation with our driver, he was allowed to enter the compound and we passed through to smaller streets. It was silent. Saudis may do their errands in the wee hours, but evidently expats do not. Next to glamorous, ornate white embassies, many fronted with fountains, hung the flags of numerous countries, limp in the still air.

"It reminds me of Embassy Row in D.C.," Mary Ann pointed out.

"There are seventy embassies inside the Diplomatic Quarter," Naif announced, proudly.

"How interesting," Mary Ann said. "I'm curious to see the houses, though."

"I don't know that we will, actually," I said. "Bill?"

"It's true," Bill chimed in. "Houses in the DQ always are obscured behind walls. Yours will be, as you know, and so will all the others."

"For security?" asked Mary Ann? "Seems unnecessary."

"More to do with Islamic custom," Bill responded. "There's a very sharp division in much of the Middle East between the public and the private, the front and the back of the house. And it's the difference between a woman having to wear an abaya all the time, versus not." We both nodded.

For ten minutes after entering the DQ our driver navigated through a seemingly endless series of roundabouts and back ways. "I'm glad we'll have a driver," I told Mary Ann. "I have a decent sense of direction, but it'd take me the two years just to learn how to get to work."

"No fooling," said Mary Ann and just then we glided to a stop. A blank, eight-foot-high wall faced the street. I assumed our driver was looking for the address; the compound looked no different from any other we'd passed, and revealed nothing of what was inside. I made a mental note of a landmark: a slender, elegant date palm tree protruding above the wall.

The entry gate swung open and light poured out. A housing rep stood by the gate, holding a set of keys and smiling warmly. We climbed out, and the rep shook my hand as he handed me one set of keys. "Welcome to your new home, Dr. Dolan, Mrs. Dolan. I trust you will be extremely happy here."

"I trust we will," I said. Mary Ann and I exchanged an eyebrows-raised look of excitement. This was it, the place we'd call home for the foreseeable future. I squeezed her arm as we stepped through the gate and into our new lives.

"I have taken the liberty of turning on the lights," said the rep, in case we had missed it. The villa gleamed. It was a grand, two-story, sand-hued building with wide, smooth walls. Windows were few and far between. Sensible, I thought, with the hope that it would be thirty to fifty degrees cooler inside than out. The grounds—and that really was the right term, not a *yard* but *grounds*—were rocky sand, but groomed, intentional. The careful landscaping struck me as all the more astonishing and pointless when I pictured a laboring gardener perfecting these grounds in the blazing sun under triple-digit temperatures. An assortment of hedges and shrubs clustered around the house in unexpected bursts of lush green. Tasteful lighting set everything in gentle glow.

"Beautiful," Mary Ann said. "Shall we take a look inside?"

At the end of a flagstone sidewalk, we pushed open a dark wooden door and were greeted by an entrance hall, carpeted with what I'd always called Oriental rugs. Adjacent to the hallway was a family room and modern kitchen. Beyond that was a formal living room, then a dining room with thick, dark woods and heavy burgundy fabrics. Wouldn't have looked amiss in a French palace. Not the breezy light fabrics I would have expected in the desert. It was all somewhat outdated (and a bit gauche), but that has never bothered me too much.

Upstairs were the master suite and, as promised, two additional bedrooms.

"Still more than we need," said Mary Ann. "I do hope the kids come visit."

"Me too!" I said, brightening at the thought. "Meaghan will really appreciate this."

"Oh *yes*," Mary Ann said, picturing our youngest exploring Riyadh. We both know that Meaghan would relish being here and would find places we wouldn't think to explore.

"May I suggest you view the garden?" the DQ official asked, as he led us back down the stairs.

Out a side door: an aquamarine oasis. *Now that's what I'm talking about. My own pool!* I realized again that I was far away from grant proposals, underfunded labs, and struggling to make ends meet. Those thoughts evaporated in the dry night air.

And next to the pool: "This is your hot tub," the official explained, and Mary Ann and I both laughed. The house had been pleasingly, refreshingly cool, and walking back outside reminded me how much technology that took.

Bill, who had waited respectfully with Naif in the front room, called out, "I've never used mine. Not once."

"I don't blame him," Mary Ann said. "I can't imagine wanting to be any warmer than I am."

"Please, right this way," the DQ official said, leading us around the pool toward what turned out to be a stunning garden. We entered through a white trellis wrapped in jasmine. I didn't know the jasmine by its appearance, but the fragrance was the same as Mary Ann's favorite tea. We strolled on, passing an immense rosemary bush and flowers and hardy desert plants of every description. The crown jewels clearly were the roses, hot-weather beauties thriving in the desert. Some boasted blossoms the size of dinner plates! We were both impressed.

"You may continue to use a part-time gardener, if you like," the official said. "A couple from Toronto also employs him."

Mary Ann and I looked around. "That seems like a good idea," I said. Mary Ann, an accomplished gardener herself, agreed. "Don't mess with success."

Back in the entrance hall we exchanged pleasantries and good-nights with Naif, Bill, and the official. I was exhausted, excited, and looking forward to experiencing our new home by ourselves, shedding my shoes and other weighty formalities.

The PSCDR staff, to our pleasant surprise, had beaten us to our home and placed our bags upstairs. "If it's OK, I'll contact you both tomorrow to set up our first planning meetings," I said to Bill and Naif.

"Of course," said Naif.

"You're not wasting any time, Terry," Bill said. "But see how you feel tomorrow once the jet lag hits."

Mary Ann laughed. "He'd be in the office *now* if he could." "I assure you, Mrs. Dolan," Naif said, "we do not all work at three in the morning. Don't worry about that. Good night to you both! And please, let me know if I can be of any service."

We watched the door swing shut behind them. For the first time since we'd come to Saudi, we heard nothing. Total quiet.

"Come on, Terry," Mary Ann said, pushing me toward the stairs. "If I know you at all, tomorrow is going to be a long day."

"What time is it?" My body felt awake, ready to go.

"Do you have the alarm clock?" Mary Ann replied.

"No, I thought it was on your side."

"Oh. Yup."

"So . . . what time is it?"

"I don't understand. 5:20. And I'm wide awake."

"Me too."

"I went to bed two hours ago."

"Me too."

The room was completely dark, but even the Blitz-grade blackout curtains were no match for the serious jet lag that woke us. Riyadh was nine hours ahead of Madison, which meant that for our still-back-home bodies it was just past dinnertime the night before. Our bodies had been twenty-one hours in transit and had no idea what to do. Unable to go back to sleep, Mary Ann and I decided we may as well start our day.

Parting the curtains, I widened my bleary eyes and instantly fell into the view. Riyadh, our new city, was waiting for us. The night before (well, three hours earlier) the boulevards had been illuminated as brightly as midday, but seeing them now in actual daylight made this new life feel real—less like a dream, more like a fact.

The sun was just rising, with regal purples and golds seeping into the villa. From downstairs, I heard Mary Ann call, "Bless their hearts! There's coffee."

I stumbled downstairs and found her already plugging in a coffeemaker. "There isn't anything else in the cabinets, but they left us a pound of coffee." With sincerity, she added, "These are good people, Terry."

Self-medicated with a few cups of coffee (necessarily black: no creamer or sugar available), we dressed for an early-morning walk. Midwesterners are conditioned always to bring a jacket. It can be balmy one moment and frigid the next. So we brought ours. Ridiculous. We swung open the door, double-checked to make sure one of us had the keys (Mary Ann did), and took about four steps down the flagstone path.

"Oh, wow."

"Yeah."

Another half-dozen steps.

"I think I'll go back and leave my jacket."

"Good idea. Me too. Maybe change into shorts."

"And your hat? Do you know where your hat is?"

Five minutes later, better equipped for the climate and, in Mary Ann's case, happily *sans* abaya since we were staying in the Quarter, we set out on our *premier promenade*.

I'd expected, without really thinking about it, that a city built *de novo* in the desert would be the epitome of strategic urban planning: something like a grid. Not so. No two streets were parallel; avenues wound and intersected at arbitrary angles. Roundabouts were fed by anywhere from two to five streets. It was unusual and laid out in a surprising and attractive manner. Another surprise was that the area was green and lush. At every roundabout, a fountain cheerfully spouted.

"The amount of water that's evaporating into the air and getting drunk by these plants is incredible," I pointed out.

"Yes. At home, sometimes we're not even allowed to water the lawn," Mary Ann mused.

A small water diversion: Mary Ann and I often wondered how all this water got to Saudi Arabia, a desert country. We found out that most of the water provided to Riyadh and other Saudi cities came from the Arabian Gulf and other surrounding bodies of water; some, like the Red Sea, two hundred or more miles away! Traveling via viaducts, the water flowed through deserts that hit temperatures of one hundred twenty degrees or more during most of the year.

Which brings me to a funny practice that is part of taking a Saudi shower. As you can imagine, the water is quite warm when it reaches its destination after its long and blistering journey. The water from the "cold" spigot, fresh from the pipes, is actually much *warmer* than the "hot" water sitting inside a home's water heater. So, when you want to add hot water you turn on the cold spigot, and vice versa.

Back to our walk. The streets were hushed. Only a few folks were out, running to stay fit. All seemed to be clad in that athletic gear that instantly wicks away perspiration. I was awed at their dedication. Running struck me as a tall order at any time of the day, never mind that here it was before 6 a.m., with the temperature on the sultry side of ninety degrees.

Each house we passed, and we passed many, was walled like ours. Behind one wall we heard children laughing and an older woman calling out to them in what sounded like Arabic.

"I suppose the walls are to keep homes' grounds private," Mary Ann noticed. "Otherwise, wow. I'd have to put on an abaya every time I stepped outside!"

As we approached the general vicinity of the DQ entry gate we began to notice people in front of each embassy: rifle-wielding, camouflage-wearing guards. I wasn't certain if they were all Saudi police or if each country brought its own security, but it was somewhat disconcerting.

Not one smiled, no one said a word or in any way acknowledged our presence. *Nice to see you, too.*

We brightened a bit when we passed what we realized was a small grocery store, the first commerce we'd seen in the DQ. Since our cupboards were bare but for coffee, we stepped in.

Perusing grocery stores abroad is always an adventure. They are at once so comfortingly familiar and so deeply foreign. This particular spot catered to the diplomatic set, with a cornucopia of products imported directly from the U.S. and Europe; in addition, there were products made locally in Saudi Arabia. My first mission was to find Cadbury Dairy Milk, not even great chocolate, but so hard to find outside the U.K. (or, at least, in Madison).

Hoisting bags of essentials—we avoided anything too heavy since the temperature was flirting with a hundred degrees—we began our stroll back to Villa Dolan. After a few detours, some intentional down scenic routes, we found ourselves again in front of our very own blank wall. Villa sweet villa. We fiddled our way in with the keys, and I thought, *This is home. This is our new normal.*

I tried to recall how long it had been—decades?—since I'd opened the door to a home other than the one in Madison.

An icy blast of relief kissed us in the face. I headed into the kitchen and dropped the bags, and as I poured us each a glass of cool water Mary Ann asked, "Do you hear that beeping?"

I stopped. I did. Every ten seconds or so, a little chirp.

"Where it's coming from?" I asked.

"Beats me." Another chirp. "Too quiet to be an alarm."

And we proceeded to do the familiar step-stop-listen, step-stop-listen to find the source of the beeps. "Low battery in the smoke detector?" I guessed, then noticed, for the first time, a cordless phone mounted on the wall. A tiny red light was pulsing.

"Hey, sweetheart, looks like we've got our first Saudi voicemail!" I pressed play and we huddled around the phone.

Professor—the recording began.

"Oh, that's Heidi!" I said. I guessed the DQ housing guy had given her our number.

I hope you and Mrs. Dolan had a pleasant trip. I want to welcome you to our country a little more formally. My parents and I would enjoy having you both over for dinner tonight. Please do come by if you are able.

She went on to give us her parents' phone number and asked us to ring her back.

"Oh, how lovely!" Mary Ann said.

I called back and warmly accepted.

"There is the small matter of getting here," Heidi said.

"It's true," I said, "We don't have our car and driver yet, but I imagine there's a way to call a taxi, right?"

"Actually, that would not be the hard part. But outside of the DQ, most houses in Riyadh don't have street addresses." This nugget of information was omitted from Naif's orientation packet. I thought again of that imaginary disgruntled urban planner. *Of course they don't.*

"No street addresses?" I repeated.

Heidi laughed. "I know. I just came back from the States and now it doesn't make sense to me either."

"How does anybody find anything?"

She laughed again. "Who knows! Well, there's an easy solution tonight. Let my family send you our driver. Please tell me your villa number and he will be able to find you."

"You don't mind?"

"Not at all!" she said. "I like to think that you are not just my new boss, but also my guest."

"Is there anything else we need to know?" I asked. "I don't think so," replied Heidi. "There's no need to bring anything. "Oh, and please tell Mrs. Dolan it won't be necessary for her to wear her abaya in our home."

"Thanks very much, Heidi," I told her. "We have so much to learn about Saudi Arabia."

"Well, *that* takes a lifetime," she said. "For now, let's start with dinner!"

Promptly at 6 p.m. a Land Cruiser—*Are these the only vehicles in the entire country!?*— pulled up to the entrance of our villa and the driver rang the doorbell. He was an African man, most cordial, with excellent English. On the drive to the Al Askary residence he told us he was from Eritrea, and that many Eritreans lived here in Riyadh. We arrived in about fifteen minutes. He pulled up to a white, two-story adobe home; it had a flat roof and was surrounded by an eight-foot-high white wall. Tall trees rising above the wall obscured any other aspects of the home.

He rang the doorbell, and almost immediately we were greeted by the entire Al Askary family—Heidi, her parents, Kaye and Alaudeen, her husband, Ahmed, and their children. What a welcome! All were wearing casual Western clothes. Heidi's father, Alaudeen Al Askary, extended his hand to me. In his mid-to-late fifties, he wore his hair quite short and sported a dark mustache. Kaye's open body language and friendliness reflected her joyful personality. Her smile was infectious. Heidi resembled her mother. She wore a cool summer dress and seemed to glow with a complexion between her father's and mother's, a permanent, subtle tan. Her husband, Ahmed, was clean shaven and soft spoken. Their two young daughters, ages two and five, were polite and charming. The family was warm and welcoming.

The entire Al Askary family engulfed us with hugs and handshakes. Perhaps it was their warm greeting or their heartfelt welcome, but we felt at home in a new country. We immediately knew they would become dear friends.

As the group moved toward the garden at the back of the house, a quick perusal revealed many nice-sized rooms. Their home reflected their heritage: European with Middle Eastern artifacts and rugs. We passed through a living room configured like a Saudi *majlis*, a gender-segregated seating area. Since male and female guests do not normally interact with each other in an Arabic home, the majlis is set aside as a room for social gatherings with guests of the same gender. In most Saudi homes, the majlis usually is adorned with large cushions along the walls and large carpets in the room's center. The Western-styled Al Askary home was an exception to this in that it was designed with furniture that welcomed guests of both genders to interact.

The kitchen was airy, and I assumed that the woman stirring pots on the stove was the Al Askary's full-time cook. Unlike many Saudi households, which often maintain five or six staff members, the woman in the kitchen, along with the driver, appeared to be the only Al Askary employees.

Other rooms on the main floor included separate offices for Kaye and Aloudeen and a den displaying Alaudeen's interests in electronic toys: elaborate stereo equipment and devices of all shapes and sizes. As we entered the back garden, we saw a small swimming pool and a patio appointed with more electronica.

Meandering through the garden, Mary Ann conversed with Heidi and Ahmed, learning that the couple married several years before Heidi went to the United States to attend graduate school at Vanderbilt University. Ahmed and the children stayed in Saudi Arabia; Heidi's parents were active in caring for the girls. I walked ahead with Heidi's parents, who met and married as graduate students at St. Louis University. They returned to Saudi Arabia after Alaudeen completed his Master's Degree in engineering; the couple had been married for thirty-five years.

Catching up with one another as a group in the family's gorgeous garden, Kaye told us. "As you know, I am American. Alaudeen is half Saudi and half Egyptian."

Ahmed chimed in, "and I am Palestinian, which makes our two children…"

Heidi finished the sentence, "human beings, of course."

As he directed us to seats around a dining table in the garden, I noticed a misting fountain, a standard Saudi outdoor amenity to keep guests cool and comfortable while they sit outside. *I've got to bring these back for my friends in Arizona!*

Alaudeen asked me if I could give them a sense of what the mission of the new Center was going to be.

"Heidi has told us a bit," he said, "but we're not familiar with the entire aim."

"Here's a little history," I began as I reached for my glass of apple juice. "About a year ago I was approached to develop and direct a research, training, and clinical center in Saudi Arabia. The main force behind the plan and the main sponsor is Prince Sultan bin Salman bin Abdul Aziz."

"A great man. We are friends, you know," said Alaudeen.

"Yes, Heidi told me," I said. "I soon learned that Prince Sultan was also a leader and the focus of the power and energy behind efforts to bring about positive change for the Saudi people." Alaudeen nodded emphatically.

"It was the Prince's view," I went on, "that Saudi Arabia may be experiencing some significant health issues in the youngest generation of its citizenry. He wants me to investigate these concerns, determine whether the Kingdom does, indeed, have those problems, and, if so, set up procedures to solve them. After Mary Ann and I made the decision to come here, the first thing I did was try to find a scientist with the right training, expertise, and bilingual skills to work with me." Alaudeen smiled as he looked at his daughter.

"Happily I was fortunate to find Heidi. So, here we are about to embark on this new and exciting journey!"

Kaye and Mary Ann seemed ready for a change of topic, and Kaye suggested dinner. Heidi, clearly paying attention to the camaraderie between her parents and Mary Ann and me, jumped up, telling her mother she would make the arrangements. In minutes, the maid joined Heidi in setting the outdoor table and hors d'oeuvres were served.

First came a course of hummus and tabbouleh, followed by fried kibbeh and kofta. Over lamb curry we discussed domestic issues such as grocery shopping, finding pharmaceutical supplies, and entertainment options.

We were happy to learn that grocery shopping was essentially equivalent to being in the States. Clothes, appliances, and most other commodities were in abundance and easy to find. Also, many drugs that required a prescription at home were attainable without one here, and at lower costs.

We were disappointed to realize that we would have to make do without entertainment options such as movie theaters or live theater; most entertainment would be dining out and going to events hosted by friends. In fact, Kaye advised us to brace ourselves for more dinner parties and social event invitations than we'd ever had in our lives. It turned out she was right.

This orientation by a family that had both Saudi Arabian and American expertise was invaluable to Mary Ann and me. They were able to answer questions we wouldn't even think to ask. For instance, Kaye pointed out that, since the Arabian calendar is lunar (the "familiar" U.S. calendar is solar—Gregorian to be precise), we would be living a different schedule. Weekends were Thursdays and Fridays. (Update: they were recently changed to Fridays and Saturdays.) Payday, every twenty-eight days, was during the "minimum moon" when one moon cycle ends and the next begins.

Kaye also gave us more information about the five calls to prayer each day, and told us the schedule changed by a few minutes every day. With only specific exceptions (for instance, when people were engaged in essential services), the country stopped what it was doing for twenty to forty minutes to show devotion to Allah. Grocery stores would close their registers and lock their front doors. Banks would stop transactions. At the Center, our staff would expect work to halt during those periods. Kaye directed us to check the daily *Arab News*, the English-language newspaper, to find out each day's prayer times. In addition, at the time of each prayer an imam's call would be broadcast throughout the city via loudspeakers, a sound that we still remember vividly.

Between bites of some of the most deliciously dishes I've ever sampled—the kibbeh alone was exquisite—I learned that some people were able to circumvent the laws prohibiting alcohol, but it was dicey. Expats could be deported immediately if they were found in possession of liquor. She added that some embassies, "and I'm not telling which," invited expats to imbibe on their premises from time to time; technically and officially, they were on the soil of their happy-hour-tradition homelands.

"So," I asked lightheartedly, "when they are not crashing embassy parties or going to friends' houses, what else do people do for entertainment?"

Alaudeen immediately jumped at the question, saying, "Oh, the Middle East is renowned for interesting archeological, architectural, cultural, and scientific treasures not to be missed! Please make time to see as many of the heritage sites as you can."

Up to this point, Heidi had maintained considerable silence, perhaps in deference to her elders. It was obvious that she had great respect for her parents.

"Heidi, what was it like leaving all of this behind to go to the U.S.?" I asked. She smiled broadly. She spoke about her time at Vanderbilt, describing her coursework and expressing confidence in her ability to assess and monitor the development of children. "My only concern," she noted, "is that my program and training was not especially 'international' in nature. It was focused primarily on the issues of North American children. I'm not sure how much will be culturally appropriate here."

I agreed this could be an obstacle, but just one of many we'd likely encounter as we began developing the project. I was taken by her thoughtful and forthright manner, and I took professional note of her interpersonal skills and intellect.

As my conversation with Heidi shifted to business, I suggested a short-term plan of action to get us started. The following day I would go to the PSCDR by myself and assess the lay of the land, find out who was already employed there, and determine what they thought their duties were. I also was eager to peruse the physical plant with Heidi and to prepare an office floor plan for administrative, scientific, and support staffs. A further step would be to set up a meeting to introduce (or re-introduce) Heidi to Prince Sultan.

Dinner was finished, then tea and mouthwatering date cookies were vanquished. Mary Ann and I concluded our delightful visit with the Al Askarys and we all agreed to plan another get together soon. Heidi told me how to reach her the following day, and their driver returned us home.

CHAPTER 15
Setting up Shop

For our first day in Saudi Arabia, the activities of exploring the DQ, unpacking, and meeting the Al Askarys were just the bridge we needed as passage to our new life. It felt a little like a vacation, as if we were getting ready for a week in a lake house in northern Wisconsin, albeit a sweltering, beer-free Wisconsin with camels instead of cows. While the process of settling in distracted my conscious mind with those tasks at hand, my unconscious was churning all the while. I was restless, almost anxious. Time to get to work.

My body clock still had not adjusted to Riyadh time, but borrowing a page from Peggy Johnson's book I waited until the decent hour of 9 a.m. before calling Naif.

As when I'd called Heidi the day before, I stumbled a bit with the phone. Phone numbers were the usual ten digits, but area codes started with "0," not the U.S. "1." Sixty years of muscle memory meant I reliably pressed "1" every time.

With my second effort, success! "Naif! Good morning!"

"Dr. Dolan. A pleasure."

"Mine as well. I'm calling to discuss logistics so we can get our work started."

"Of course," he said, and I heard what I thought was mild surprise, as though he hadn't been expecting this for another week or two. "How can I help?"

"First, I'd like to meet with Prince Sultan, at his convenience, but hopefully soon. I would like him to meet my chief assistant, Dr. Heidi Al Askary."

"Naturally," said Naif, "and His Highness also looks forward to welcoming you back to his Kingdom. Allow me to check his calendar and get back to you."

"Wonderful. Second, would you direct me to the appropriate person to contact at the Center? I'd like to visit today and re-introduce myself. It's been a while since my first visit."

"By all means." Without pausing to think or look anything up, he answered. "Our contact's name is Ghazi Al Shalon." I recalled meeting Ghazi on my earlier visit. "I shall give you his mobile number when I call you back."

As promised, Naif called back no more than half an hour later. He gave me a time the following afternoon to meet with Prince Sultan and also Ghazi's contact information.

After unpacking the rest of our suitcases and putting out a few personal items like photographs and artwork, I went to find Mary Ann. "All right, love, I think it's that time."

"*Now*?" she asked, incredulously, arranging clothes in a bureau. "It's one in the afternoon. You're walking over there *now?* Just call. They'll send a driver."

"I have to at least *try* the walk. It's only supposed to be fifteen minutes, not even a mile."

Mary Ann smiled. "I know you like the summer in Wisconsin, my love, but…"

I'll admit I can be a bit headstrong, especially when it comes to doing things on my own. "I just hate the idea of being dependent on a driver," I said. "It's like I'm fourteen again, waiting for my mother to drive my friends and me to the soda fountain."

"Well then, it's a good thing you didn't grow up in the middle of the desert."

A few minutes later, a half-liter of bottled water in hand, sunglasses donned, head wreathed in a twill hat, I pulled open the door. BAM!

It was cool and pleasant inside the house, but I swear I could hear a sucking sound, like when you open a freezer, as I pulled open the door. I couldn't imagine this furnace blast would ever feel normal to me. The air smote me—that's the only word for it, *smote* me—full in the face. I confronted the desert like it was a fire-breathing dragon, took a cool slug of water, squared my shoulders. I was ready. I stepped off the porch.

Fifteen minutes later, having drained the water and, undoubtedly, sweated it out again, I bounded through the Center's automatic doors and sighed at the soothing, icy air. Later that night I admitted to Mary Ann: "You know what? I think having a driver is going to be just fine."

As I removed my sunglasses in the Center's lobby, I was startled. I rocked back on my heels. In front of me was an office not caught up in its usual busy hum, or even one in postprandial lethargy. No, instead, I found the entire staff waiting for me: fifteen people, each with hands primly folded, lined up diagonally across the lobby. All that seemed missing were tubas, a drum, and a one-and-only base. Instead, these men—yes, all were men—were wrapped in crisp light fabrics, nearly motionless. Surprised, I stared at them for a second, still panting with the effort of my thermal walk. My Oxford shirt was sweat-sodden, face red as a rare steak. *First impressions are everything!*

With seamless grace my goal in mind, I walked forward, hoping to say something respectable. In all my decades of running labs, I'd never been received by a staff *in formation* before!

It also would seem they forgot the memo about smiling.

Alright! "Hello!" I called out, as brightly as possible. "Have you been waiting long?" It was peculiar to me that they'd been waiting at all, and now I imagined them standing there since my call to Ghazi an hour earlier.

"Not at all, Dr. Dolan," a man said, stepping forward and proffering his hand. "I am Ghazi Al Shalon, His Highness's representative at the Center. We met during your previous visit. It is our honor to welcome you back."

"Oh, that's very kind of you," I said. "I remember you. The Prince's representative, you said?"

"Yes," and did not go on, as if being the "representative" of Prince Sultan was all I needed to know. "May I introduce you to the staff?"

"Of course! Please do." I began to get my feet under me. Emboldened by the ceremony, or the absurdity, of the occasion, I announced, "And smile, guys, will you? This looks like a receiving line at a wake." Whereupon they did smile, politely so. *Maybe Muslims don't have wakes?*

Ghazi walked me down the line, making introductions as if I were reviewing the troops. "Khaled, our Information Technology Supervisor, Majed, Chief Accountant; Ahmed, Director of Purchasing…"

I noticed the names all seemed to be Muslim, but Ghazi was the only one wearing a thoube. I assumed he was the only Saudi. The others seemed to be expats, apparently from countries like Pakistan, the Philippines, Indonesia, sub-Saharan Africa, the 'stan countries, and the rest of the Arab world.

At the end of the line, I figured out the ordering protocol: the least-skilled labor was last. "Gulraiz, Marcos, and Azamat, chauffeurs" and "Riek and Mahmoud, coffee servers."

I turned and surveyed the assembly again. Don't ask why. I figured this is what I was supposed to do. It was an incredible mix of nationalities but from our limited conversation, everyone seemed to be English proficient. I realized, only now, that I had unconsciously assumed that Center's *lingua franca* would be English.

"Thank you all," I announced, not quite sure how to break up the reception without yelling *dis-MISSED*. "Please, don't let me distract you from what you were doing."

No one moved.

I saw one or two puzzled looks.

Umm. OK. Better try something else.

"Please feel free to return to the work you were doing before." That worked: the troops quickly fell out in different directions to return to their desks where their workloads were probably pretty manageable... for now. As I considered their so-far not-too-busy days, I wondered whether a country that outlawed theater and music performances allowed solitaire and *Minesweeper* on workplace computers.

"May I show you around the Center?" Ghazi asked. I gladly agreed.

The main floor of the building formed three sides that enclosed an outdoor space. That courtyard, about twenty-five feet by twenty-five feet, was tastefully landscaped with desert plants.

The first room on the tour was a sizeable vacant office. It was inhabited only by furniture: at the desk was a leather chair suitable for a Bond villain. Scattered around the office was a variety of seating areas and tables adorned in a frilly, faux eighteenth-century style: in all, it resembled a petite European palace. It was just shy of ostentatious, which I had come to realize was pretty much the norm for a Saudi executive office.

"If you wish," Ghazi said, "this could be your office."

"Thanks, Ghazi. I'm sure it'll do."

The tour continued through the rest of the first floor, but frankly, there wasn't that much to see. Prince Sultan had dedicated sizeable real estate to this effort, but not much had been done with it yet. Apart from a large room housing the clerical functions—made up of an entirely male staff—the space was pretty empty.

This didn't discourage my tour guide.

"And here we have an empty room; it could be an office or a meeting room as you see fit," he said in one doorway, then stopped, waiting patiently.

"Yes, very good," I said, and we moved on.

"Here is another empty room."

"Yes, so it is," I said.

"This too is an empty room," he said.

" Ghazi, do we have a *lot* of empty rooms?"

"We do!" I noticed that we hurried past one rather grand and clearly inhabited space, bedecked with more heavy wooden tables and floral Louis XV *fauteuils*; that was undoubtedly Ghazi's office.

The second floor was much the same. We revisited the conference room where I first met Prince Sultan. I also viewed a prayer room, sparse but inviting, windowless, with warm dim lights and Persian carpets.

The tour concluded, we descended the main staircase, a grand affair that curved elegantly around an atrium of white stone. At the bottom, I asked, rather jauntily, "Would you care to join me in *my office*, Ghazi?" I added that there were some logistics I was hoping to go through with him.

We returned and arranged ourselves on the somewhat formal but comfortable furniture. I rummaged through meticulously organized desk drawers—*that would never last*—and found a pen and a legal pad which I gave to Ghazi. "You might need this," I said.

"I would appreciate you taking care of a few things so we can get started on our mission," I told him. "First, some kind of space for women to work." His head, which had been nodding, became motionless. "I expect you'll know best what's appropriate, but, it's something we'll need to see about soon. Dr. Heidi Al Askary, our new Deputy Director, starts tomorrow."

"Dr. Dolan," Ghazi said, protesting and puzzled but gracious, "Excuse me, perhaps you do not know our customs, but it is not possible to have the women working here alongside the men."

"Thank you, Ghazi. I understand this isn't typical, but the project requires participation from women colleagues."

"And she is *Deputy Director*," Ghazi went on, not seeming to have heard. I wondered if he was more troubled that she was a woman or that she had a fancier title than he did. "Forgive me, but do you have the permission of His Highness?"

"As the Director of this Center, it's my prerogative to recruit and hire those I feel are necessary to accomplish our goals. And this was my decision. I understand this may be controversial. But please be assured, I've consulted with the Prince as well.

"The uninhabited wing of the building on the far side of the courtyard—could that not be the women's wing?" I chose to not mention that the Prince had been the one to suggest this working arrangement for women.

Ghazi grudgingly agreed. From there, I took a checklist from my briefcase and discussed the remainder of the logistics, point by point.

One of them was that Heidi and I would need mobile phones with international service. I had no idea if all mobile phones had such service, but I knew that our experts lived all over the globe, so I needed the capacity to reach across time zones.

The Center had a secondhand Land Cruiser, and my next request was that Ghazi obtain another that could be at my disposal. The five-minute ride was going to feel silly and make me self-conscious every day, but just thinking about the recently-endured morning walk made me feel overheated again. Besides, I was sure I would be traveling to meetings throughout the city.

I asked Ghazi which member of the staff would be most appropriate to serve as my aide and driver. After a couple of tryouts of others on the staff, it turned out to be a fellow named Yahya as the individual of choice. I asked that he be detailed to me. I knew that Yahya and I were going to be spending a lot of time together, and I hoped he'd be as gracious as the Al Askary's driver. Last, I asked Ghazi to give the current staff a heads-up: they should be flexible for the first few weeks so we could have face time when I could get to know them better.

Ghazi's head bobbed in response to these items. Then he suddenly realized he should be writing this down, and his attention snapped to capturing every word. As a Westerner, it was amazing to me to watch someone write so quickly from right to left, the Arabic convention. At last, he looked up. "This is everything, then, Doctor?" he asked.

"For today," I said, with a smile, perhaps a bit impish. For now, I felt we had ample strategy but were short on operations and furniture.

He wasn't even out of my office before he reached for his mobile phone. I expected he couldn't wait to share with Naif his incredulity about women on staff.

I smiled. Part of me accepted my role as a guest in this country. And, to a fellow like me, raised in the Midwest, that means not making a nuisance of oneself. We don't complain about the décor, or a hard mattress, or the way the coffee's made even if it tastes like oven cleaner. But I knew, or hoped, that I was *more* than a guest, that I was here to make a difference; and change was part of that mandate. If I didn't like the coffee I was going to make my own. Tomorrow we would see how well it worked out.

I spent a little more time getting acquainted with my office, setting up my computer account, finding supplies. I had done this before, but the last time, setting up an office in Wisconsin, had been many years ago.

After a few hours, I decided to head back to see how Mary Ann was faring on the home front. As I stepped from my office, one of the two coffee servers hurried toward me, undoubtedly fearing they had been too slow with my joe. I indicated "no thanks" and strolled out toward the reception desk. The plan was I'd gently interrupt and politely ask if any progress had been made on finding me a driver. But no sooner had I entered the lobby than the fellow at reception, a young, dapper South Asian man, rose respectfully and asked, "May I be of service?" Truly, these words felt like a caricature of deferential service, and I couldn't imagine that any Westerner had spoken that phrase in fifty years. Again, I knew I was in a different world.

CHAPTER 16
Yahya and the Safeway

My ride, a brand new white Toyota Land Cruiser, pulled up on the other side of the Center's doors. (I knew it was mine because the man at reception told me so; white Land Cruisers are as plentiful in Riyadh as yellow cabs are at La Guardia.) Knowing it would be about fifty degrees hotter outside, I braced myself, stepped out gingerly, and grunted a little as the inevitable inferno whacked me across the face. I was immediately distracted from my discomfort by the man who hopped out and ran to open the door. Distracted first by the fact that he could run in this heat at all; distracted second because he was well over six feet tall and muscular as a young tree. He smiled, his teeth white against his very dark skin.

"Good afternoon, Dr. Dolan," he said, waiting patiently while I climbed in, then gently closing the door behind me.

"Would you mind taking me home?" I asked him once he was inside. "I'm living at… hang on a moment…" I started fumbling in my briefcase for my villa number, just to be sure I wasn't transposing any numbers.

"I have already been told," he said. He seemed satisfied as he said it. I thought with incredulity that he might actually be eager to have the chance to drive me. Not a typical reaction in the States, to be sure!

A few minutes passed in silence. This man likely would be Mary Ann's and my driver, responsible for our safety on a daily basis, perhaps for years. At the first red light, I turned toward him.

"I think we should be properly introduced," I said. "Terry Dolan."

He proffered a hand larger than our dinner plates, once again flashing his smile. "I am called Yahya," he said.

"A pleasure to meet you. Where're you from, Yahya?"

"Sudan! Do you know the place?"

"I haven't been, but it's close by, right?"

"Just over the Red Sea, past Ethiopia," he explained. Now I could picture it—just below Egypt. "I am from the capital, Khartoum, where the Blue Nile and White Nile join."

"That must be an old city," I said.

"Oh, yes!" he said with pride. "One of the oldest. I am building a house there."

"You're building a *house?*" I asked, then felt mortified by how condescending my surprise may have seemed. A few friends in Madison had built their own houses—or rather, had them built—but they were radiologists or Fortune 500 officers, not drivers.

Yahya didn't seem to notice. "And when I retire, all my children can visit, and my brothers and sisters can all live there, too." *OK, so we still have our differences,* I thought with a smile, picturing my siblings and all our families living under the same roof. I am from South Dakota and South Dakotans are usually pretty unflappable folks, but by Day Two we'd be fighting over how crispy the bacon should be.

"How many children do you have?" I asked

"Five!" he said. "They live with my wife and me here in Riyadh." I leaned further between the front seats and saw five portrait-style head shots of brilliant-eyed, smiling children. *I guess that answered my question about photos being OK in Islam.* The youngest was still swaddled and wearing a tiny white cap.

It was only with a modicum of alarm that I noticed this charming photo display was just behind the steering wheel; that placed it, I realized, in *front* of the speedometer.

I sat back, resigned. Living in Saudi Arabia was going to be about adjustments: learning to live and let live. Besides, I immediately felt safe with Yahya.

Once we reached Villa Dolan, I peeked inside to ask Mary Ann if she was ready for our first real grocery shopping adventure. Not the corner store this time, but the real thing!

Twenty minutes later we were strolling slowly down the aisles of our first Saudi Safeway. The sign outside was identical to those in the States, so I assumed this store would be the same as back home. Not so much.

Eyes wide open in amazement, we perused this arena of comestibles. We felt like time travelers from the past or aliens from another planet.

The store was endless, exquisite. It brimmed with every food ever eaten, anywhere. The meat counter alone was longer than some Olympic track events, and was organized by animal and country of origin.

"Do you like it?" Yahya called out. He was trailing behind us, jovially pushing our shopping cart. He took his "driver" designation seriously. "You should try the Irish beef. It is very good!"

We turned into an aisle. "I've never heard of some of these grains," Mary Ann said.

"I haven't heard of some of these *countries*!" I retorted. "Yahya," I asked, holding up a box, "what's farro? Is this any good?"

"Oh yes!" he said. "It is from Italy. My wife uses it for salads. You cannot find that in Khartoum!"

"Or Madison, I think," Mary Ann muttered.

We were spelunking our way through the produce aisle when our reverie was broken by a call to prayer: a gentle alarm, like a tiny bell, rang out over the store's speakers. Yahya had advised us *en route* that afternoon prayers began at 3:13. (I still wonder how Saudi Arabia sets all its clocks to precisely the same time.) "You may stay in the store," he had said. "But no one will be working, at the registers or anywhere."

"Ten minutes to prayer time, Doctor," Yahya said.

"Guess we'd better scoot then, love," I said to Mary Ann. In minutes, we had checked out and Yahya had loaded our treasures, even the most dubious, into the back of the Land Cruiser. "Next time you *must* try pomegranate molasses," he urged.

"You know what I was just thinking?" I asked Mary Ann, turning to look at her in the back of the SUV. "You know how we've heard that call to prayer at 5 a.m. the last few mornings?"

"I know, I know," she said. "Once my body clock is back to normal, I hope I'll be able to sleep through that."

"No," I said. "I meant, think about it: Muslims all over the world pray five times a day, every day, rain or shine. Even at 5 a.m., they get up and go to the mosque, like we saw everyone doing today. 5 a.m. here. 5 a.m. in Madison…in January!"

"Oh, wow!"

I shook my head with admiration. "I mean, we go to church every Sunday, but these people! 5 a.m. every day. Even when it's ten below zero. Kneeling to be humble before God."

"That's what 'Islam' means, I think," she said. "Submission." She must've seen the look on my face. "What? I know where the library is, Dolan!"

I laughed.

"You're right, though," she said. "It's amazing. And I feel guilty complaining about the loud voice of the *muezzin* who sings the call to prayer. How early does *he* have to get up?"

We later would learn much more about the role of prayer in the typical Saudi Arabian's life. For instance, we found out that just as weather reports are posted daily in every newspaper in the West, daily prayer schedules are included in the Kingdom's news sources.

After our first prayer experience at the Safeway, we also came to learn of the fervor of Islamic prayer and its profound significance in everyday life. Each morning, well before sunup, loudspeakers throughout Riyadh would reverberate for several minutes with the spine-tingling imam call.

Trust me, no matter where you lived, and regardless of whether your windows were open or shut, you woke immediately. I only recognized the words *Allahu Akbar*, but the entire call was mystical...beautiful.

The call alerted all men to go to their nearest mosque to pray—or if that wasn't possible, to pray at home or wherever they were at the time. Women primarily prayed at home; children with their mothers. The final daily call occurred sometime after sunset.

During our time in the Kingdom, we learned more. We knew that Islam is a monotheistic religion, that there is one God, Allah. In talking with new friends, we found out the Qur'an teaches there were many great prophets, including Abraham, Jesus, Moses, and others. However, the greatest prophet was Muhammad. Interesting to Mary Ann and me, perhaps because we are Christian, is that Muslims believe Jesus was a great prophet and his early role was to prepare us for Allah. They also believe that Jesus was born to Mary in a virgin birth. In fact, in Islam both Mary and John the Baptist are highly revered.

Muhammad, born in the 600s, was illiterate and so the long-deceased Prophet Abraham spoke the teachings to him. Muhammad presented those teaching to his followers. Today, approximately 1.5 billion people, one-fifth of the world's population, are followers of Islam.

CHAPTER 17
Consanguinity 102: Science and Culture

Back at the center, Heidi and I were just about ready to formulate a plan to screen newborns in the Kingdom for diseases. First, though, here's a little essential background information about consanguinity, both the science of shared genomes and some cultural implications.

Genetic health relies upon inheriting properly arranged pairs of DNA, and inborn errors happen when DNA strands are incorrectly duplicated. We see inborn errors in DNA duplication much more often when couples are closely related to one another than when they are not.

But how close is too close? Early in the study we were confident in our hypothesis that the increased incidence of inborn errors in Saudi Arabia was related to marital consanguinity. While precise definitions of consanguinity vary, at the simplest level a consanguineous marriage is one in which the husband and wife are related.

Reality is not that simple though, and complexities abound. To some degree, we're *all* related! For the human genome, like the genome of any other single species, much of it is the same for all individuals in that species, with only slight variations between different members.

Deciding where to draw the consanguinity line is arbitrary, and determined differently by different cultures. In non-science discussions, some cultural (and legal) codes classify a seventh cousin as a consanguineous relative, a vanishingly distant relation by many standards. In some discussions lines are drawn at second or first cousins. But science is not a friend of ambiguity. In order for research into the epidemiology of genetic diseases to be consistent and meaningful, science had agreed on a particular definition of *consanguineous*.

We decided in our project to set first-cousin relationships as a benchmark. I should add that there are many other groups that have set second cousin as a standard. Our in-house decision was partly based upon the fact that, in Saudi Arabia, there were so many large families that the number of second cousins in some families might be less manageable and even confusing to young married couples.

Table of Consanguinity

Showing degrees of relationship

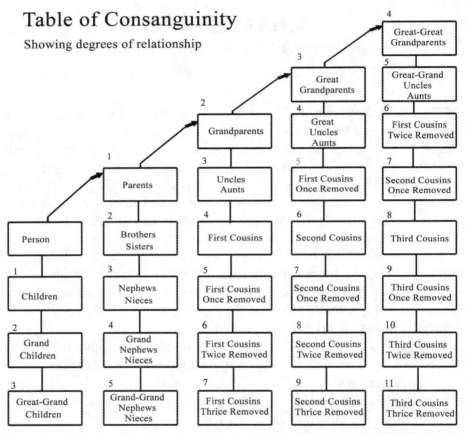

Table of consanguinity and degrees of relationship. Knot System recreated here with permission from Knud Højrup.)

Projections on the effect of consanguinity

In a classification called the Knot system,[6] the closeness between parents and children is assigned the value one. Siblings who share a parent are two; aunts and uncles are three; and first cousins are four. So for any given individual, a person assigned a value greater than four would be a

6 K. Hojrup "The Knot System: A Numeric Notation of Relationship," *National Genealogical Society Quarterly* 84, no. 2 (1996): 115.

second-cousin or a more distant relative.

For our purposes, we defined a consanguineous marriage as between spouses who have a Knot system value of four or less; or first cousins.

Before beginning our study to test for inborn errors in the Saudi population, we used world health data projections to get at least a reasonable estimate of the numbers and probable distribution of to-be-expected births of babies with inborn errors in that population. (Although information *about* Saudi Arabia's population is difficult to come by *in* Saudi Arabia, outside agencies have developed statistical estimates to generate reasonably accurate data.)

Science cannot accurately predict on a case-by-case basis whether a specific marriage will result in inborn errors due to consanguinity; said another way, no one can know ahead of time where in the genome a random misalignment may occur. However, we *can* estimate how many children will be born with anomalies by using two groups: children born to parents who are not first cousins, and children born to parents who are first cousins.

Here's the math, with statistics and estimates. In Saudi Arabia, approximately 500,000 babies are born each year. Based upon a few published studies, we estimated that half of the parents of those 500,000 babies, some 250,000 couples, are non-consanguineous. For comparison, the rate of non-consanguineous marriages in the United States is around ninety-seven percent or higher. (Note: U.S. estimates vary, and in many cases such marriages are no longer closely monitored.)

From world health studies, we estimated that one in 1,500 Saudi Arabian babies born to non-consanguineous couples had an inborn error. So, our projection was that about 167 babies would be born *per annum* with inborn errors to non-consanguineous parents (250,000 divided by 1,500).

Now we looked at the other 250,000 couples. If, say, the incidence of inborn errors found in babies born to these consanguineous parents is one in 300, the number of babies born with inborn errors would be 833 (250,000 divided by 300).

So, the total number of babies with inborn errors among the 500,000 annual Saudi Arabian births would be approximately 167 + 833 or 1,000 per year. If no marriages were consanguineous, 500,000 births would yield only 333 babies born each year with inborn errors versus 1,000 per year with the marriage of first cousins. The effect of consanguinity over a ten-year period would be the birth of some 6,600 children.

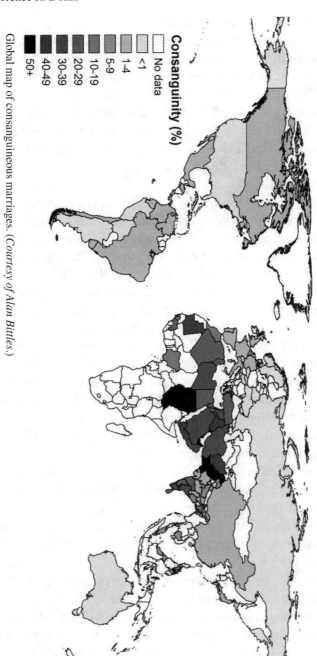

The geography of consanguinity

Global map of consanguineous marriages. (*Courtesy of Alan Bittles.*)

Consanguinity (%)

No data
<1
1-4
5-9
10-19
20-29
30-39
40-49
50+

These inborn error predictions are skewed significantly low because our estimates reflect screening only for fourteen diseases. The number of babies identified would dramatically increase when the program reached maturity and more diseases were screened.

About 1.5 billion people, twenty percent of the world's population, practice Islam. Roughly twenty-four percent of Muslims reside in twenty countries in the Middle East and North Africa (355,000,000). Although not all consanguineous marriages occur within Islam, recent studies show that nearly one-half of Muslims in this region are in consanguineous marriages,[7] suggesting that approximately 177,500,000 of those people are members of marriages that produce significantly higher offspring of infants with genetic diseases and/or disabilities. The remainder are dispersed across the globe. For example, sects or branches of most major faiths—Judaism, Christianity, Dravidian (generally South Indian) Hinduism, Buddhism, Zoroastrianism (or the Parsi religion), various Confucian sects—practice consanguinity to some degree, with the notable exception of China. In China, national policy rigorously and successfully has opposed marriage among relatives. Lastly, the Hmong (an ethnic group from China, Laos, and Thailand) belong to one of eighteen clans and have a particularly complicated system for consanguinity. Marriage within a clan is expressly forbidden, but the clan is defined as the *father's* family. Children have no such affiliation with the *mother's* clan, so while children may never marry members of their father's family, their mother's family is fair game. Children are in no way forbidden to marry family members of the mother's clan.

Why marry a cousin?

All scientific estimates suggest that consanguineous marriages are more likely than others to result in babies with inborn errors. So why do some people and nations continue to practice this tradition?

The question of why people marry their cousins is an important one that may help to drive an eventual solution to the dramatic problem of inborn errors. As you can imagine, our team discussed this question at length among ourselves as well as with leading scientists around the world. We believe there are a few primary reasons why Saudi Arabians,

---

7 G.O. Tadmouri, et al., "Consanguinity and reproductive health among Arabs", *Reproductive Health* 6 (2009):17.

in particular, unite in consanguineous marriages.

First, at the time we were launching the newborn screening project in Saudi Arabia, most people in the Kingdom didn't know that a consanguineous marriage could be dangerous. Maternal and child health programs were in their infancy, and most issues related to newborn health were unexplored. First cousins who married generally did not expect negative biological consequences for their children.

Second, Saudi culture exists within a tight weave of tribes and large families. Marriages usually are arranged among parents and families, with prospects drawn from this tribal and familial pool. Outsiders rarely would be considered.

A third reason, I would discover later, is that sometimes the blood relationship of a betrothed couple involved first cousins who were strangers. If, for example, the parents of the married couple each came from a family of twenty or so, and if each of the siblings of the parents in turn had a large family, it is conceivable that hundreds of first cousins may be unknown to each other.

Another reason: marrying a first cousin can solidify an already-existing compatibility of values, religious practices, and lifestyles. Relationships with one's in-laws, often less than ideal, are already a known entity: they are already family. Networks of love and support are well-established and probably have weathered tests of time and tribulation. If disaster strikes (e.g. spousal health problems, severe sickness, or death of a child, etc.), family structures already are in place to provide support.

Finally, consanguineous marriages make it easier to manage legal and financial issues surrounding inheritances and property. In the West, this advantage may be negligible. But in a country without a constitution and without even an inchoate legal structure to resolve disputes, serious disagreements can arise. Sometimes, when the person across the negotiation table is family—someone with whom a relationship will be ongoing long after the dispute is over—both sides are more motivated to work toward a solution, rather than battle for a short-term gain at the other party's expense.

A misconception

As already stated, the majority of consanguineous marriages in the world are among Muslims. This sometimes leads to a misperception, particularly in the Western world, that the practice of consanguinity derives from an Islamic directive. It does not. The Islamic religion does not promote, encourage, or condone consanguineous marriages.

The bottom line

For hundreds of years, consanguineous marriages and Saudi Arabia have gone hand in hand, and for many practical reasons. While the Qur'an does not promote consanguinity in any way, a bevy of cultural and familial reasons *do*. It's clear that Islam is *not* the explanation.

What do we anticipate may happen if/when individuals *do* come to understand the possible medical risks to their children from consanguineous marriages? Some countries provide betrothed couples with counseling about the inherent risks prior to marriage. These types of programs are just beginning at the time of this writing. But it's still common for couples to make the same choice with eyes wide open. When weighed against tradition and the benefits of marriage within a known social network, the apparent security of consanguinity may trump ephemeral concerns for the health of yet-to-be-conceived children. To repeat, no one can know ahead of time when random misalignment of genes may occur, and known positives usually inform a decision more than unknown negatives.

CHAPTER 18
Getting Down to Business

The morning following our grocery adventure, Yahya was waiting for me outside the villa at 8 a.m.

At the Center, I began the day by introducing the staff to Heidi, a task I was both eager and anxious about. I wasn't certain how well she'd be received by an entirely male Muslim workforce.

"Good morning, everyone," I said. My voice in the silent room was as loud as a starting gun. "Let's get this thing going."

No one said a word while we waited for stragglers, but I easily imagined the first thing everyone noticed was Heidi standing by my side in her abaya and headscarf. Not only was she before them as their leader, she was also on hand to repeat or clarify, in Arabic, any points I made in English that were not clear to them. This would mean that many of the staff would receive their marching orders from a woman—perhaps for the first time since they were children heeding their mothers. *No problem there!*

If all went anywhere close to the plan, this was the *least* of the changes we'd be bringing to the Kingdom.

"Good morning, everyone. I've met most of you already, and as you know, I'm an American neuroscientist with a research focus on childhood diseases. This is why Prince Sultan asked me to come to Saudi Arabia. It's my pleasure to introduce Dr. Heidi Al Askary. Her expertise is in children's development. Like me she has a Ph.D., and she will be our *Deputy Director*." I'd learned enough by this point to make sure everyone understood the title. The room, if attentive-looking, was stony and still. *Tough audience.*

"Together, we all have a united mission. Some members of the Royal Family are concerned about the health of the children of the Kingdom. Some believe the incidence of diseases among children is higher here than elsewhere in the world. Our job, the job for *all of us*, is to figure out whether this is the case." Heidi jumped in and translated. I assumed she was repeating, and maybe expounding a bit, in her Arabic translation.

"Today is the day we get started. However long it takes, we're going to figure out whether this Kingdom is in danger and what we can do about it." I noticed, some members of the staff began to nod as I spoke. I continued to make eye contact, tracking slowly around the room, just as when I was lecturing in a classroom. The looks I saw were attentive, open. My confidence finally stirred, coming to life.

"Dr. Al Askary and I already have been working to find out what progress, if any, the Kingdom has made toward understanding the incidence of genetic diseases here and to figure out what *we* should do. We've got an extensive plan."

I waited again while Heidi translated.

"The short answer to the first question—what has the Kingdom done so far?—is, well, we have investigated maternal and child health programs in the Kingdom. What is done here for expectant mothers? What kind of care is available? How extensively are fetuses examined *in utero*—ahh, in the womb—to gauge their health? Unfortunately, these services are nonexistent. We're still reaching out, but so far, there hasn't been much to find.

"Second, we assessed newborn screening programs. These are complex programs that test children for genetic diseases shortly after they're born. Without them, it's almost impossible to know the who, what, and where of birth diseases: who is sick, what they have, and where they are.

"These screening programs, with the exception of one small program don't exist in Saudi Arabia, which means we have no data on Saudi births. We are starting from square one. And we will have to gather that data from all over—from Riyadh and Jeddah, from every corner of the Kingdom. That's why we all are here. We're going to figure it out, all of us, together.

"So, roll up your sleeves because we're going to start, from scratch, our own nationwide newborn screening program. I'll be forthright with you: it won't be easy. Based on estimates from world health institutional data, approximately 400,000 to 500,000 babies are born in the Kingdom every year. Thankfully, many are born in cities where at least there's infrastructure to help us set up a screening program. But many births occur where there is no such infrastructure. Our program will not be considered a success until we've reached babies born in cities and villages, and those born to Bedouins in the desert. No one," I added, with probably unnecessary emphasis, driven by all the inequality I'd already seen. "*No* one is beneath our notice or unworthy of our help."

I paused, then interrupted myself, apologetically. "Maybe some of you are wondering just what exactly a screening program is, what it involves. I'll explain in much more detail tomorrow. I appreciate you bearing with me." A few more heads in the room nodded. I know the look of a student who is trying hard to understand, but isn't quite getting it. Some staff were lost. This was my area of expertise, not theirs. But I could see that their efforts to keep up were sincere.

"Still, a screening program is just the first step. It doesn't help much to diagnose the disease unless we're going to do something to treat it. That's the second part of our job: to set up monitoring and treatment programs for children with genetic diseases. When there *are* treatments, we must ensure they're administered correctly. Where there aren't…well, that's where we do the best we can. We track the child's progress, for better or worse, and help their families give them the best care possible.

"But even if we *can* treat many of these diseases, we're just closing the barn door after the horse is gone." Heidi paused in her translation and seemed to search her mind for a parallel. *There are horses in Saudi Arabia, right?*

I chuckled. "Sorry. It's solving a problem that has already happened. What we really want to do is prevent these diseases. So the third part of our mission is to look into possible triggers for each disease. We need to find the causes. They could be genetic, but they could also be environmental, or could even come from bacteria, viruses, or parasites."

I took a breath and looked around the room to make sure most people were still with me. "Finally, once we've figured out the causes, we will address prevention. I'm talking about national campaigns to educate people and intervene where it makes sense.

"There's no way we can complete this all in a year." I saw relief sweep the room. "Maybe not even ten years. Maybe not even in our lifetimes! It's a project bigger than any one of us. But every step makes the children of the Kingdom safer and healthier. Please be patient, and when things get difficult, as they likely will, know that the work we are doing here together is for the good of Saudi Arabia's future."

I surveyed the room one more time. Our PSCDR staff was beginning to see the purpose in their work, it seemed, and they were eager for more. It wasn't patriotism that was moving them. After all, nearly the entire staff were strangers in a strange land. Instead, it was humanity. I saw that the project was in good hands.

Heidi and I were scheduled to meet with Prince Sultan after lunch, and we prepared for that meeting. She was to have a primary role in this project, and though the Prince already knew her family, we agreed it was important to provide him with a comprehensive briefing of her professional background.

We also spent time that morning exploring the PSCDR physical plant, discussing options to organize the space most efficiently. Thankfully, the building was arranged so it would be easy to divide workspaces between genders and equally easy to facilitate whole-group interactions—mixed gender—when required.

I thought it would be nice to have Heidi join Mary Ann and me at the villa for lunch and asked Yahya to take us. I overlooked the fact that in Saudi Arabia, it is forbidden for a man (other than a driver or family member) to ride with a woman alone. The consequence could be arrest and imprisonment. If injustice of the discrimination against women was not sufficient to rouse my ire, certainly the logistics would be! It occurred to me later that Yahya must have been deeply concerned, but he said nothing.

Following lunch, Heidi and I (water bottles in tow) walked the short distance to Prince Sultan's office. As far as I could tell, walking alone with a non-related woman is OK. Riding in a car is not. *Don't ask.*

Always gracious and friendly, the Prince's staff greeted us and escorted us to his office. "Welcome, please come sit," he urged with a smile. "It is a pleasure to see you again, Dr. Dolan and Dr. Al Askary. Tell me, he said to Heidi, 'how is your father?'" Alaudeen had served as the Saudi Ambassador to Hong King and Chief of Protocol in the Ministry of Foreign Affairs. "And I understand from Dr. Dolan that you are quite accomplished in the sciences."

Heidi enthusiastically told him of her studies, highlighting their relevance to the project. The Prince, who had studied in the U.S., particularly enjoyed questioning Heidi about current events in the American university realm. "Perhaps you know," he mentioned, "the Kingdom recently launched a program to send Saudi students to American universities. Nearly 30,000 students already are participating, and plans are underway for the program's continued growth."

He went on. "And speaking of great success, please Dr. Dolan...the project at hand. Is everything as you wish with the new staff?"

I replied in the affirmative and updated him on our progress and the morning's meeting.

"I appreciate the magnitude of this endeavor," he said somberly, but brightened, adding, "But I am confident we have exceptional minds leading this charge, and I sincerely thank you both. If there is anything else you need to move the project forward, please let me know immediately."

CHAPTER 19
The Game Plan

Promptly at 9:30 the next morning I reconvened the staff in my office. After yesterday's speech, I wanted everyone to know they truly were part of the team, that yesterday's speech wasn't just a pep talk. As I did as a professor at Madison, I wanted them to know they could visit me in my office whenever the need arose.

Today was an opportunity to walk them through some of the finer points of the plan, after absorbing the big picture the day before. What follows is the gist of those points.

Most of my PSCDR staff did not know about the miraculous technology that is tandem mass spectrometry (TMS). So I explained how we would be able to determine, for an entire nation, those who had a genetic disease.

Tandem mass spectrometry. In the 1950s, pediatrician Dr. Robert Guthrie studied the lack of the enzyme *phenylalanine hydroxylase* in the blood of newborn infants. That lack indicated the presence of phenylketonuria, a potentially deadly disease that, left untreated, could cause mental retardation and serious brain damage. Knowing a child lacked this enzyme made treatment possible before any harm came to the child. The treatment was simple—a diet devoid of phenylalanine. But how could one screen children to find out if the enzyme was lacking? We needed an economic and mass-scale technology to detect the missing enzyme. That technology was tandem mass spectrometry, and its invention by Guthrie in the 1960s is among science's most important technological breakthroughs.

When TMS was first developed, it became possible to screen for twenty developmental genetic diseases. The diseases shared several general characteristics: visibly undetectable at birth; inherited because of an aberration in the genetic materials from one or both parents; caused by the absence of either a specific amino acid or acylcarnitine (transporter of fat) in the blood of the infant.

Specific amino acids and acylcarnitines are needed to produce particular proteins necessary for healthy development of tissue, muscles, organs, or blood, or to produce an enzyme whose job it is to destroy toxins. The new technology allowed us to determine when one of these amino acids or acylcarnitines was missing.

How does TMS find the presence or absence of these critical ingredients? The answer lies in measuring weights: the ingredients are comprised of molecules, and the technology is based upon knowing the actual weight of each of these molecules.

A tandem mass spectrometer and accompanying equipment used to assess the concentration of the various amino acids and acylcarnitines being screened. The image on page 128 illustrats the results of a typical acylcarnitine profile. (*Courtesy of Patrice Held, Wisconsin State Laboratory of Hygiene.*)

The device employs a two-step process (the two steps are the "tandem" part of the name TMS) to ascertain the number and magnitude (that's the "mass" part of the name) of certain molecules in a newborn's blood sample. For a test, a drop or two of blood is taken from a newborn at birth. The drops are spun in a centrifuge-like device at very high speeds. Imagine tossing a pocketful of change on a flat surface, then spinning the surface very quickly. The coins will be distributed depending upon their weight. Lighter dimes don't travel to the outside as far as heavier quarters and stay closer to the center. The heavier coins travel further out away from the center. The same idea occurs for molecules in a blood sample! Knowing the weight of each of the molecules we are studying, we can ascertain whether the correct amount of the molecule is present in the blood based upon the distance it travels. (That's the "spectrometry" part of the name).

If a particular component travels further than it should, it indicates that an above-normal amount is present; a smaller distance indicates a shortage.

From one drop of blood, TMS reveals whether a baby has an abnormal amount or type of substance in its blood. If so, further analysis tells us which disease is present.

The following graph illustrates a TMS-test result. The horizontal axis represents molecular weights from low (left) to high. The vertical axis shows the range each molecule moved. This spectral distribution depicts the results. Voila!

Impressed by this technology? It gets even better. TMS analyzes blood samples very, very quickly. Within a few hours of sending 1,000 or more blood samples from newborns to a centralized spectral analysis lab, you can have a complete analysis! The molecular presence or absence of several dozen compounds is known within an hour or so! For each newborn! Amazing.

In 2002, an international panel of physicians and scientists, experts in genetic diseases, convened to discuss how to standardize screening and, ultimately, treatment. The panel developed a worldwide recommendation that a total of twenty-nine diseases can and should be screened for and treated.[8]

Across the globe, newborn screening programs have come to be seen

---

8 An additional twenty-five diseases can be detected by screening, but were considered a lower priority for detection because no known treatments exist. Another group of twenty-seven diseases were known to exist because of their symptoms, but the diseases' biology was not well understood at the time and no screening methods existed. Over the ensuing dozen years, some disagreement has emerged. Whether or not a disease is considered treatable, for example, depends on the level of technology and resources required to treat it. As a result, the list of treatable diseases varies country by country. Some countries screen for all detectable diseases, regardless of whether or not anything can be done about them (some states in the U.S. screen for upwards of fifty diseases).

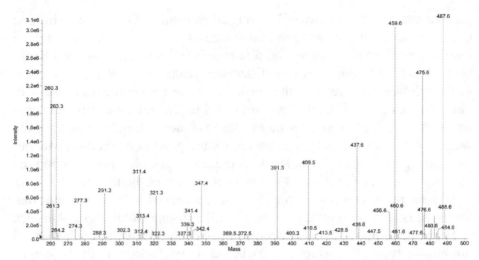

Depiction of the results of a typical acylcarnitine profile obtained from analysis of a filter paper dried blood spot. On the abscissa is the distribution of mass for approximately 40 different analytes that are being screened. On the ordinate is shown the magnitude of each analyte. The concentration of each analyte is determined by comparing the magnitude of a given analyte to the magnitude of a standard at a known concentration. (*Courtesy of Patrice Held, Wisconsin State Laboratory of Hygiene.*)

not only as humane and responsible, but also economically sensible. The initial investment, while considerable, is far less of a financial burden than treating the full force of genetic diseases.

Today, screening is a triumph of the medical community. Almost universally in North and South America, Asia, and Europe, newborn babies are screened for inborn errors of metabolism.

But in Saudi Arabia, again, with one small exception, there were no newborn screening programs. We had our work cut out for us.

Back to our 9:30 meeting. As a reminder from the previous day, I showed the group what I had already written on a whiteboard:

Goals for the PSCDR Newborn Screening Program:

• Ascertain incidence of diseases in newborn and young children. Many diseases cannot be seen but can be tested for.

• If a newborn child has a disease for which we are screening, immediately put the child into a treatment program and monitor the child's intellectual, physical, and behavioral development. Provide counseling support to families.

• Assess possible causes of the disease(s). That may involve environmental evaluation, viral and other medical issues, family-history exam, and genetic assessment.

- As more is learned about diseases and causes, conduct national educational and intervention programs to promote prevention.

Those were the overall goals we wanted to accomplish once the screening program was established. Before that could happen, though, we had to set up the program from scratch.

On a separate whiteboard, I wrote tasks as I talked through our team's initial steps, again with Heidi translating and clarifying.

First, I wrote Step 1. *Outreach*. I explained, "This means our Center staff will visit each birthing center in the Kingdom, from world-class hospitals in Riyadh to clinics in the Rub al' Khali. There are/will be approximately 220 hospitals and more than 1,900 health care centers in the Kingdom that address the needs of pregnant women and their newborns. About eighty percent of these are/will be administered by the Ministry of Health. The other twenty percent are/will be served by a dozen or so other entities. We're estimating 450,000 births per year in the birthing centers and an additional 50,000 or so births in Bedouin areas.

"With the blessing and support of Prince Sultan, we will visit each site and secure approvals from its management. Once we have these approvals, we'll visit each facility again to teach the staff how to gather blood samples. It's a simple heel-prick for newborns and tiny blood samples from each parent.

"An important part of that second visit will be to show the staff how to store the samples for transport. We'll teach them, if they don't know, how to conduct a series of newborn clinical exams, including hearing and visual tests.

"Finally, we will show clinicians at each birthing site how to gather brief histories of the parents. We'll show them how to follow our questionnaire so we can determine whether the parents are related and if they have other children. If so, we'll find out if these other children are healthy or have shown signs of genetic diseases; and whether any other potential genetic diseases have appeared elsewhere in the family. From that collection of blood samples, exams of newborns, and clinical histories—once we analyze the data—we hope to have as complete a picture as possible."

To conclude the discussion, under *Outreach*, I wrote a to-do list and continued:

Staffing. Staffing. Staffing. "We need pediatricians, nurses, clinical support personnel, computer technicians, you name it!—Hundreds of positions need to be filled."

Communication. "We have to convince people to participate. We need clear and compelling materials, publicly endorsed by the Royal Family, for parents-to-be and for OB/GYN nurses and doctors, about why participating in this assessment is so important for the health of the Kingdom's children."

I continued, and wrote, Step 2. *Storage and transport.* "Samples and data do not have to be stored for long. We will be expanding a testing lab at King Faisal Specialist Hospital and Research Center. More on that later. But part of our job is to find reliable transportation to ship samples and data to the lab in Riyadh every forty-eight hours."

Step 3. *Testing and analysis.* "We will staff and equip a laboratory at King Faisal Center. Technicians will run tests to see if any of the diseases for which we are screening are present. We will focus on amino acids as well as molecules called acylcarnitines. These will provide immediate evidence of inborn errors of metabolism. A lab confirmation of an inborn error will immediately trigger an action plan designed to minimize the impact of the disease on the child's life."

Under *Testing and Analysis*, I wrote: Equipment and Technology: Tandem Mass Spectrometer and computer network.

Step 4. *Inborn Error Assessment.* "If an inborn error of metabolism is found, we will develop strategies to monitor the continuing health of the infant. When smart phones becomes available, we will provide the child's mother with one (we were anticipating that technology would be available in the near future) and sufficient training so she is competent and confident in one particular feature. We will program the phone to ask, on a regular basis, a series of questions about the baby's welfare that require only a yes or no answer. We will record and log these responses at the Center for future analysis."

Step 5. *Treatment.* "If the disease is one that can and should be treated immediately, we will direct the parents to a well-resourced hospital as close to them as possible, what we call a 'tertiary-care center.' For treatable diseases that are less urgent, and for those diseases we cannot treat, our team will refer the family to a counseling program. Another important step is that we will notify the original birthing-site staff so they can handle any follow-up care. These locations, closer to where the parents live, should make it easier for the parents to be dutiful about follow up."

This game plan, as monumental as it was, included only the steps we *anticipated* we'd need to take. We knew we would be in for some surprises and obstacles along the way, but we didn't yet know what they would be.

I looked around the room once more. I saw eyebrows raised, heads shaking, one man even had his hands to his face in astonishment.

I laughed to break the tension. "It's a lot, to be sure. But we have a clear idea of what we need to do. We have an extraordinary team already assembled here," I gestured to the group. "And, many more recruitments planned. Plus, we have the full support of Prince Sultan. I know this is a lot to take in, but I'm here to answer your questions now, or after you've had time to think about all this, or at any point, any time. Over the next few weeks, we'll analyze and discuss all this, set ourselves some specific objectives and timelines, and assemble work teams."

CHAPTER 20
Marshalling the Ministers

The Monday following our kickoff meeting, I waited in a Ministry of Health conference room. It was the same facility I had visited during my initial trip to Saudi Arabia. Today I'd be meeting with several of the same officials, but this time I was hoping to get them sufficiently invested in our project so they would loan me some staff members.

I had allocated several hours for what we expected could be a marathon meeting, perhaps even getting down to details and schedules. My objective was to make clear that the Center couldn't make any meaningful progress until we launched our newborn screening program and analyzed the findings. And, most importantly, we needed their support and assistance.

Based on my previous vague and politically "careful" meetings with the Ministers, I had my concerns. Turns out, I was pleasantly surprised.

The entire Ministry staff was well-credentialed and even included two physicians and a population sociologist. They were completely on board with the idea of newborn screening. The group was comprised of scientists with a record of scientific publications and academic training from either North American or Western European universities. What's more, the Ministry staff and management must have discussed the matter prior to this meeting, and had already agreed about the critical importance of the project; they had even come to agreement that care of newborns should include a family-level understanding of inborn illness.

The Ministry team appreciated that if the government later decided to conduct a more thorough census than previously, the screening program would be a head start, supplying essential demographic data.

My role in the meeting was to provide an overview as well as a perspective based on my prior experience with projects like this one. The

Ministry understood the program in theory, and I would be able to walk them through logistics.

So often, the devil is in the details.

I explained, "It's our recommendation, based upon the best practices in North America and Europe, to screen for roughly thirty diseases." I noticed a few furtive glances around the room as though they were deciding who would be the one to speak up.

The wheel stopped at the Minister of Health.

The Minister of Health cleared his throat. "Dr. Dolan, I'm afraid we respectfully disagree with that recommendation. We believe that screening for thirty diseases is excessive. It may have been a priority in the West, but it isn't for us. We currently have the ability to treat only fourteen diseases, so we cannot waste our efforts screening for double that number."

I pushed back, gently. "This is true, but wouldn't we want to *know* if children have other diseases? That way, if and when treatment becomes available, we can help them."

Without responding to my argument, the Minister replied, "It is our opinion that screening for thirty is unwarranted at this time. For now," and he pushed a piece of paper toward me, "these fourteen are sufficient."

Choose your battles, Terry. Choose, your battles.

Grateful that such a list even existed, and knowing that we had support in so many other areas. I didn't push the topic. I did, however, come to an understanding that the issue of screening for other diseases would be tabled for future discussion.

Thankfully, disagreements did not become a pattern. We shared the outline of the operational plan Heidi and I had devised, and the Minister and staff offered general support.

The Minister's staff listened actively, asked perceptive questions, and were, in short, far better prepared to be full partners in this process than I'd ever dared to hope. The last item of business was to assemble a steering committee to oversee the entire program. The Ministers agreed to a seven-member group; that group included Heidi and me.

Inch by inch.

We also managed to borrow a population sociologist and two physicians from the Ministry of Health. Our Center, it would turn out, now had its own data scientist whose services would be crucial to the program. He would be the focal point of all data analysis, giving final examination and approval to all results.

Only a week in, prospects already were looking good.

That evening, at home with Mary Ann, I poured two glasses of our finest Saudi "champagne" and we toasted: "To progress!"

CHAPTER 21
A Visit to the KFSHRC

Another important collaboration was between our PSCDR and the King Faisal Specialist Hospital and Research Center (KFSHRC). Heidi and I were a bit anxious about our meeting with the Hospital team because much was at stake. The facility had an excellent reputation, and progress for our program hinged upon access to their staff and facilities. Thankfully, we were not disappointed.

We already knew that Dr. Sultan Al Sedairy, the KFSHRC Director, was an internationally lauded administrator who had received his M.D. and Ph.D. from Columbia University. We also knew he was related to Prince Sultan. At the meeting we found he was not only a ready supporter but would be an active participant in the program.

As we entered the building, Dr. Al Sedairy greeted us with a hearty, "Dr. Dolan, Dr. Al Askary, welcome to the KFSHRC." He continued: "I'm very excited about your project and I've been looking forward to meeting you."

"Thank you, we are so happy to hear that," I replied. "And we are eager to collaborate with you."

"May I show you around our facility?"

"By all means, yes."

As we walked around the massive and modern building, Dr. Al Sedairy introduced us in turn to his team—molecular biologists, neurologists, and geneticists—whose services he offered in our newborn screening work. In particular, he introduced us to Dr. Mohammad Rashed, director of the TMS facility, who would be fundamental to the success of our entire program. We were heartened when Dr. Rashed enthusiastically told us, "It will be a personal and professional honor for me to use TMS to help newborns and families."

Heidi and I were as impressed with the hospital's facilities as we were with Al Sedairy's esteemed staff, and were delighted that the staff's interests and experience seemed to dovetail perfectly with the Center's mission.

A step forward.

We returned to the Center buzzing with adrenaline. A huge to-do list awaited us, but now we had access to a state-of-the-art facility that surpassed my expectations, and we had entered a partnership with an internationally acclaimed team of collaborators.

Next step: recruit staff! Pediatricians, nurses, and clinical support personnel; physical and occupational therapists; computer technicians and administrative and operational personnel; and coordinators associated with each and every birthing site. Immediately, before anything else, we needed a human resources director to coordinate them.

Heidi and I discussed our objectives. "With regard to staffing, we need a point person, someone who can coordinate the on-site programmatic activities," I explained.

She agreed, adding, "someone Arabic-speaking, with a medical or social work background, and preferably female. This person has to feel comfortable interacting with the mothers of newborns."

"Definitely. Furthermore, she should have sufficient technical expertise to explain the program to physicians and nurses as well."

We knew our outreach would be for naught without a formal statement from the Prince documenting his sponsorship of the program and explaining who we were.

We agreed Heidi would take the lead to find our on-site coordinator. She would also write a project overview and letter of introduction for the Prince's signature.

Just a few days later, mild-mannered Heidi exploded into my office in an unprecedented fury.

"No wonder this country can't get anywhere in the world of commerce! Stupid rules and protocols!"

"Oh my goodness! Heidi, please sit down. What's going on?" I tried for a calm tone, though I have to admit I was worried. Heidi was usually the calm eye of any storm, definitely not quick to temper.

She sat and took a breath. "OK, it's about the recruitment and payment of our staff. According to the Saudi government, we have no say about our own staff's salaries! Their pay depends completely upon two things: their title and the country where their passport was issued.

"Slow down. Give me an example."

"OK, say we want to hire a Director of Human Resources who has four years of experience. We can pay that person between $45,000 and $24,000, depending on their home country. If they are from the U.S. the maximum salary is awarded, followed closely by Canada, Great Britain, and Western Europe. The amount decreases significantly if the person is from South America, Africa, or other Islamic countries. Even Saudi Arabia! It wasn't the case for me, but I'm learning now why so many young Saudis get their educations in the States. They live there long enough to get an American passport, then return home and earn double or even higher than if they never got the passport."

"But that's ridiculous!"

"Oh, it gets worse." She shook her head with an anger-fueled grin. "You're going to love this. Even though you are the Director of the Center, you can't give raises or bonuses to your employees based on performance. You can conduct all the performance reviews you want, but that won't affect pay raises. They are entirely dictated by the system."

I shook my head with angry frustration. "Well, no wonder the Kingdom has a reputation for lackadaisical employees. There's no monetary incentive for a job well done."

Just at that moment, the phone rang and caller ID indicated Bill Cornish. *Maybe he'd have insights!* "Heidi, please excuse me, it's Cornish. I'm going to take this. Maybe he can tell us something. In the meantime, let's try to move forward on staffing, and see what you can do about the outreach materials." She nodded, rose, and walked back to her office.

"Hey there, Bill. Just the person I wanted to talk to. I'm hoping you can clarify something for me."

"Sure. Shoot."

"I just became aware of *more* staffing constraints and wanted to see if you could shed some light. Heidi tells me we have to follow a pay scale determined by an employee's native country, or at least where their passport originated. That's unfair and strange in itself, but I was flabbergasted to find out that Saudi employees aren't even near the top of the pay scale. Westerners are! What gives?"

I stopped for a moment, but when Bill didn't immediately respond, I continued. "Remember our phone call months ago when you told me it was important to some members of the Royal Family that I hire more Saudis? I didn't like the restriction, but I complied. Now I'm being told that Saudi citizens are not allowed to earn as much as Americans, Canadians, and Europeans! Bill, this is absurd. If it was so important that I hire Saudis, wouldn't the Kingdom want them to receive competitive salaries?!"

A long silence.

"Terry, I wish I had the answer to that." I imagined he was shaking his head. "You're right. It's counterintuitive and unfair. I don't know what to say, except it's the way of conducting business here in the Kingdom."

I sighed. "I'm also told I can't determine my own staff's raises! Evidently I can conduct all the job evaluations I want, as long as I don't try to reward my employees for jobs well done!" I was getting hot under the collar.

"Yes, that's about the size of it. Listen, I know how frustrating this is, but I hear that the Prince is pleased at the strides you and your team already have made. I have gone through much of this myself, so all I can recommend, Terry, is to stay focused on your ultimate goal and work around some of these obstacles. Even when they seem bizarre."

I tried to focus on my larger task and what we'd already accomplished. "I know. I know," I sighed, calming down a bit. "You're right, Bill. It's just so confounding. Listen, thanks so much." As my thumb started to move toward the END CALL button, I paused with embarrassment. "Wait, Bill. I'm so sorry. I got carried away. Are you still there? *You* called *me*! What's going on?"

CHAPTER 22
Transportation and the Desert

Laughing at my single-mindedness, Bill replied. "Well, since you asked, I was calling because I think you should take a hike. Literally. And now I see the timing is perfect. You need a change of scenery."

I sighed in agreement. "Indeed, I do." And time outdoors would be just the thing. "Definitely!"

An intrepid adventurer, Bill was a member of an international trekking organization. In addition to seeing more of the country, he said, a hike also would be a chance for us to test what my new Land Cruiser could do.

We met at our villa the following Thursday morning at 7 a.m. (I was getting used to the fact that Thursdays were our new Saturdays). The early start was to allow a more comfortable foray into the desert.

When you think desert, what's the first word that comes to mind? Sand, right? And sure enough, I thought we'd encounter sand, waves of sand, sand dunes, windswept sand, lots of sand. You get the idea. But as we drove south out of Riyadh toward what is called the Empty Quarter, there wasn't any sand in sight: the terrain was rough and rocky.

And it was *wadi*-ful. What's a wadi? It's a deep canyon caused by erosion, millennia of erosion. These were walled by sheer cliffs, 600 to 800 feet high, some even higher. And this 250,000-square-mile Empty Quarter really lived up to its name. No readily apparent civilization, no roads, not even unmarked trails. Needless to say, traveling cross-country requires some pretty high-tech breadcrumbs—a navigation system and GPS—so you can retrace your steps.

Once underway I peered into each of the four directions and saw they were virtually identical. It would be easier than falling off a log, or in this case, a cliff wall, to become stranded in this labyrinth of wadis. Bill told me that each year many expats do just that: become stranded and are never found. *Thanks for mentioning that, Bill.*

Speaking of Land Cruisers, I must sing their praises for a moment. They really are exceptional bits of machinery for cross-country travel, and it's easy to see why the Saudis love them. But there were two things about them that were especially interesting to me.

First, the central compartment between the driver and front passenger wasn't just storage…it was a refrigerator! *Certainly handy for desert travel.* Its lower compartment made ice cubes and could keep a meal fresh for several days. *Genius!*

Second, the vehicle had two gas tanks. The gas cap security flap covered two twist-off lids, each one going to a separate tank. Driving on the highway or across the desert and run out of gas? No problem. Just switch a button on the dash and the car switches over to the backup tank.

Just don't try that trick twice.

Now, getting back to the Empty Quarter. Two-hundred-fifty-thousand square miles, roughly the size of Texas, of barren desert: virtually no towns or villages, rare running water or electricity, and bereft of civilization in the way most Westerners think of it.

One thing you *do* see in the desert—camels. On our little sojourn, Bill and I saw hundreds, and I wondered if they were wild or domestic.

"Camels pretty much are Bedouins' only worldly possessions," Bill answered. "They are their life-blood. They rely on camels for milk, meat, clothing, shelter, and medicines. Acidic camel urine is used as an antibacterial, and, you'll appreciate this, Terry, newborn babies are bathed in it to prevent illness. *Which is fine, but I can assure you it will not be part of our newborn screening protocol.*

"So, are there…I don't know…camel ranches or do they just roam?" I asked.

"A little of both. Bedouins can recognize camels that belong to them. They don't brand or mark them like they do at home, and we're talking upwards of one hundred camels owned by one family."

The Empty Quarter isn't entirely so. It's estimated that some 400,000 Bedouins live in the Kingdom's deserts, and further, that there are approximately 4,000 desert births per year.

So, where were these elusive Bedouins?"

"They seem to live in two primary arrangements," explained Bill.

"First, in enclaves. About three to five families live together, almost entirely out of view of passersby."

We did spot some of those enclaves later on our hike. The gatherings were dotted with four-walled, tent-like structures made of what must have been camel hide. The materials looked thick enough to provide some protection from heat and cold. One type of tent appeared to be for cooking, another for sleeping.

"Since custom dictates that men and women not married to one another can't cohabitate, the men tend to sleep outside," explained Bill. "Often you'll see another structure, a kind of majlis, a gender-segregated sitting room designed for socializing. Those rooms tend to be used exclusively by men.

"Second, Bedouin sometimes live in villages, usually with a small building at the center which serves as the communications hub to the rest of the Kingdom. In fact, in cooperation with the United States, Saudi Arabia has been working to develop power and communications capacity to improve connectivity. It is those capabilities that enable medical services to be in contact with the villagers."

Our mission in establishing a newborn screening program for the Kingdom was to assess every baby, including those who enter the world in one of Earth's most desolate places, hours from modern medical resources and with little in the way of technology. Not long ago the transportation and technology barriers would have been more difficult to overcome. Today, most Bedouin enclaves share a pickup truck that serves the community. They use the vehicle for transport to and from birthing centers, for other medical care, and for goods and for supplies. On more than one occasion Mary Ann and I saw a camel in the bed of the truck—completely at ease, sitting upright, being driven over some of the rockiest, bumpiest terrain I've ever seen.

And especially interesting about Bedouins and pickup trucks: women are most often the drivers! As Bill informed us, Bedouin men often are occupied with out-of-enclave work in the desert, so the women are in charge of transport. While there are rigid cultural restrictions on women driving in urban areas, clearly, practicalities overrode such restrictions.

To provide newborn screening to every Bedouin family, we knew that a communal pickup truck would not be enough. We had to come up with a comprehensive plan to reach them, to encourage their initial interest, and to ensure their ongoing participation.

At the Center, while we were working toward hiring a coordinator to arrange on-site services across the Kingdom, we were also working diligently to provide health-trained service providers in the field to conduct initial evaluations. The desert was a good metaphor for the current state of health service in the Kingdom, and it would prove a most formidable task to develop oases of care.

We also needed reliable transportation—a way to whisk samples back to Riyadh from even the most remote places. Securing this transportation system proved easier than we expected. Once we had identified our shipping origins—no less than all the birthing centers and hospitals throughout the Kingdom—the next step was to find the best delivery system.

We invited representatives from delivery-service experts—FedEx, UPS, DHL—to meet with us to discuss our program. In each case, we briefed them on our needs for transporting human biological specimens in cooled containers from sites around the Kingdom to our laboratories in Riyadh. We assessed their track records and invited their proposals.

Within weeks, we were in final negotiations with DHL. They'd never been involved with a program involving human specimens and were intrigued and excited to get the program going.

A few more weeks and we were ready to run a test involving three cities: a city in the north (Buraydah, population 600,000), a city in the south (Al Kharj, population 400,000), and a city in the southwest (Abha, population 360,000). We believed those three locales would give us a reasonable distribution of the incidence of inborn disease as well as a good geographic scope to test the transportation system.

Because Bedouin communities were smaller in relative population, we wouldn't require regularly-scheduled DHL service to these areas. Rather, upon a Bedouin birth, a van would be dispatched to that particular location the very next day.

We all shared some skepticism at the beginning of our program about how well the transport aspect would work. To our delight, this part of the newborn screening program proved to be a great success.

CHAPTER 23
Law Enforcement, Legal and Religious

It was just a few days before Meaghan would arrive in Riyadh, and Mary Ann and I were discussing some of the logistics of her stay. In perusing the daily English-language newspaper, the *Arab News*, I found an article about a demonstration by women in the cities of Riyadh and Buraidah that led to the arrest of twenty-eight women and children.

According to reports, the women were demonstrating on behalf of their husbands who had been imprisoned for extended periods—sometimes more than ten years!—without attorney representation and often without formal charges filed. There simply was no due process of any kind. The article suggested that the women were asking only that some formal legal action take place.

Returning to the office the next morning, I voiced my concern about this to Heidi. We often discussed the Kingdom's cultural, social, and religious issues, and I was always concerned about the lack of basic legal rights in the Kingdom. I asked Heidi whether she thought those legal issues could impact the Center. She recommended confidence with a dose of caution. We had the Prince's full support and we conformed to Saudi expectations, but it never hurt to be careful.

I also couldn't help but think about my own daughter's impending arrival here. The news about the demonstrators seemed another example of how women and families were second-class citizens in the Kingdom's legal system.

A much more disturbing event occurred in 2002 in Mecca when fifteen female students burned to death in a dormitory fire. According to reports, the *mutawa*—an organization of sometimes questionably-appointed religious "police" who monitor public behavior—would not unlock the exit doors because the young ladies were not properly attired! The fire occurred at 8 a.m. and in all likelihood the students were already dressed, though that's beside the point. All these young women died, tragically and horribly, because of a cultural belief and the decisions of conservative men who put themselves in charge.

This was Heidi's homeland, but she too was alarmed by such an atrocity. We continued our work with a cautious eye. With regard to prenatal care and testing, Islamic rule at the time forbade a fetus from being touched or interfered with in any way. Our study did not include any such measures (not even amniocentesis), but we realized we could easily be subject to scrutiny. Later, when we left Saudi Arabia, a loosening of Islamic law would afford health care practitioners a little more leeway and options.

CHAPTER 24
The Golden Rule

O ne of our favorite Saudi excursions was to a famous souk, or shopping area, the Deerah Souk. Two new friends, Jack and Susan Chandler, from Seattle (Jack, a physician, and Susan, a neurophysiologist), were carpet aficionados. The four of us frequently went to the souk.

Before modern malls came to Saudi Arabia, souks were *the place* to shop in the Kingdom. The Deerah Souk, in the middle of Riyadh, is adjacent to the main square and is also next to the city's most important mosque. It also happens to abut the Masmak Fortress, the base conquered by young Abdul Aziz bin Al Saud in 1902.

The souk is home to some two hundred stalls and small shops. It is always bustling with activity—all types of authentic merchandise ("somewhat expensive") and not-so-authentic merchandise ("get ready to bargain"). Perhaps more than anything else, the souk is evidence that Saudi Arabia is a commerce hub on a still-vital trade route between the East and West. Two categories we saw the most were carpets and gold.

The array of colorful carpets was spellbinding—from Afghanistan, Iran ("Persian" rugs), Turkistan, Pakistan, and other countries in and near the Caucasus Mountains. Fortunately for us and our living room floors, many merchants spoke English (we learned how to bargain) and were entertaining and informative about their wares.

Strolling amongst the vendors, we met a young man from Pakistan who, with his brother, traveled the international road, seeking carpets handcrafted in villages and refugee camps. The brothers told us they acquired antique carpets; some, held in families for decades, were heirlooms now for sale due to war and poverty. They managed a kind of trade relay. While one was abroad finding merchandise, the other remained in

Riyadh to oversee sales. About every six months they would switch roles.

Jack and Susan provided us counsel as we shopped. Many older carpets were noted for their superior quality—900 knots per square inch, their patterns representing tribes from myriad nations. They truly are works of art. (Mary Ann and I recently moved from Madison to the Chicago area, and several of those lovely carpets grace our home there.)

It may be true that all that glitters isn't gold. But in this souk, that wasn't really true. With the exception of rugs, gold was the item most readily for sale. We were dazzled by jewelry of every shape and size.

Saudi Arabian gold is darker and of higher quality than the kind usually found in the States. And, here's another interesting nugget. In Islam, keeping gold is a wise and popular way of saving money. Banks do not collect or pay interest when money is borrowed or invested. For most Saudi families of modest wealth, investment opportunities are limited to international banking or keeping gold. Once, watching an elderly woman walking slowly through the souk burdened by the weight of gold necklaces, I remarked to Mary Ann, "She could be wearing her family's life savings or her granddaughter's dowry around her neck."

The topics of life savings and necks lead me to another place near the souk: one also buzzing with activity, but focused on punishment, not purchases.

The souk is located on the main square in Riyadh, a plaza also known as "Chop Chop Square" by many expats. The plaza is where capital punishment is meted out. Beheadings.

Saudi Arabia is one of about five countries that still continue this practice.

In years past, beheadings were held when the crowd peaked, which was Fridays after midday prayers. Some may call it progress that they now occur any day of the week at 9 a.m. and are not announced ahead of time. Yet, horrifyingly, people congregate at that hour every day. You know, just in case. *Something like a "gapers' block"—traffic slows while drivers gape at an accident on the side of the road.*

I won't go into the gruesome details. Disturbingly, these beheadings have been videotaped and posted on YouTube. However, I will share the story of a well-known executioner interviewed for a story in *Arab News*. According to the piece, this man is regaled throughout Riyadh and around the Kingdom. He was quoted as saying he is at peace with his work, sleeps well at night, and believes he simply is carrying out the will of Allah. He's not troubled by beheading one or even six prisoners a day, and is especially proud of his...shall we say...precision.

Saudi Arabia is a land where trades are passed down from one generation to the next, and this man was gratified that his son would follow in his footsteps.

But it was the story of money that got me started on this topic. In this case, blood money. When crimes lead to capital punishment, the victim (or victim's family) may negotiate a fee to be paid in lieu of the perpetrator's head. The accused pays the fee; the victim officially forgives the accused; the court dissolves punishment; the prisoner is free to go. *Talk about a price on one's head!*

In the "good old days" those sums were moderate, but in recent years they've reached staggering amounts, into the tens of millions of dollars. But I know as a Westerner not to shake my head with moral indignation; I know that in my own judicial system, a defendant's fate—life or death—can be determined by how much he shells out in legal fees.

Mary Ann and I were simply appalled by the practice and sought to find out how public beheadings could still continue in this day and age.

We scoured articles in *Arab News*, Amnesty International, U.S. State Department reports, and other publications. A Walrus Foundation article detailed that more than 1,000 beheadings took place since 1985 (U.S. execution rates for that period are only slightly behind this). We learned the practice is based upon Sharia Law, the moral code and religious law closely related to Islam. In recent years, an accused could meet his or her death for adultery, sodomy, drug trafficking, treason, rape, or prostitution. Perhaps the most serious crime of all is apostasy because it involves learning about Allah, and then rejecting him.

In its strictest application, Sharia Law is considered an infallible Law of God. One of the primary concerns of Westerners is that the law is applied by imams and religious leaders, not trained judiciaries.

Another issue is a legal system tainted by bigotry. Just as capital punishment is applied disproportionately in the U.S., beheadings are more prevalent in Saudi Arabia for migrant workers, male or female, and for ethnic minorities. In fact, female domestic staff can face death for retaliating against a physically abusive employer. At one point, we read that forty-five foreign-born maids were on Death Row awaiting beheading.

A front view of our villa in the Diplomatic Quarter in Riyadh.

The living room and kitchen areas of our villa.

One of many examples of the talents of Anwar, our gardener, along the side of the villa.

Another view of our residence's gardens.

Our gardener, Anwar, originally from India, standing in the backyard of our villa.

Our trustworthy and admirable driver, Yahya, originally from Sudan, in front of our residence with Meaghan and Mary Ann.

With my dear and extraordinarily capable associate, Dr. Heidi Al Askary.

Dr. Al Askary with her husband, Ahmed, and their two children.

It is difficult to tell which is more uncomfortable—the rider (me) or the camel.

Meaghan using a common mode of travel in the desert.

The majlis (sitting room) at the weekend residence of Prince Sultan bin Salman.

A semi-business gathering in Prince Sultan's summer garden. The attendees included Prince Sultan on the left; Dr. Sultan Al Sedairy, third from left; and Bill Cornish, second from right.

A "formal" dinner setting in Saudi Arabia—sitting on the ground with a blanket for a tabletop.

My two closest American colleagues while in Saudi Arabia: Dr. Fred Wightman (center) and Dr. Steve Schroeder (right).

Mary Ann leading an all-expat hiking group down the side of a wadi. This is a good example of the terrain in some areas of the desert.

Two hikers precariously sit on the edge of a wadi approximately 800 feet deep.

My key associate and colleague, Mary Ann, in her abaya.

Meaghan and Mary Ann in typical public attire for Saudi Arabia.

CHAPTER 25
A Few Steps Forward

Focusing on work helped distract me from some of the Kingdom's upsetting cultural and religious realities. Our progress on the newborn screening project was slow but steady. Remember, we were starting a nationwide program from absolute zero, with substantial obstacles lurking around every corner.

Overcoming these challenges, whether anticipated or a surprise, made us feel especially proud of our progress. Just a few weeks after our frustrating conversation about staff pay levels, Heidi managed to secure qualified Saudi applicants for the on-site coordinator position and the HR director. A bonus was that our HR candidate, Maya Raffi, a bilingual Lebanese woman, knew of more candidates for a variety of administrative and clerical positions. We didn't waste a moment hiring Maya and several of her contacts.

What's more, Heidi inked a preliminary draft of outreach materials. I agreed that it persuasively summarized the purpose of our project: to assure the best chances that every birth in the Kingdom would be a healthy one.

In the materials she explained what was needed to achieve this goal. We planned to find out the extent to which newborns and toddlers had evidence of inborn diseases. Heidi knew costs to families, birthing centers, and labs would be an immediate concern, and she insightfully highlighted that testing, transport, and analysis services would be paid by our Center. She explained that additional services might include follow-up examinations of blood samples and behavioral tests to track how children were progressing through specific developmental milestones. Truth be told, Heidi and I were a little giddy with our progress.

I called Ghazi and asked him to schedule a meeting with the Prince at his earliest convenience. I wanted to discuss the outreach materials with him. That meeting was successful, and with the Prince's approval, our materials were ready to go. Our newly-hired on-site coordinator arranged personal visits to each birthing center to walk their staff through our plan. The "outreach" portion of our game plan was moving at a respectable clip.

It was time to confront the Center's technology issues.

We knew we needed a sophisticated computer network, software and hardware that could analyze and integrate data from birthing centers around the country. But neither Heidi nor I had expertise in purchasing, setting up, and servicing such a system. When it came to computer technology, we were both eager to defer to experts.

A longtime colleague and friend, Dr. Frederic Wightman, was a recent retiree in North Carolina. He also happened to be one of the most capable computer experts I knew. I called and told him, in elaborate detail, what we needed to accomplish. Forty-eight hours later, Fred Wightman shared his comprehensive plan for "machinery" and "personnel"—what system he would create for us and the kind of human resources we would need to use it.

Fred understood that our work would involve sensitive, confidential, human health data. Privacy and backup were equally essential, so he suggested that workstations update—automatically and daily—to an offsite storage system over a secure connection.

And, since many of our potential families would have Internet access, Fred thought a web presence would be a valuable outreach strategy. I mentally added "webmaster" to the burgeoning list of staff members we'd need.

CHAPTER 26
Press Perspectives

Living and working in the Kingdom was complex, just like every other place Mary Ann and I have ever lived or visited. We spent many an evening at home, sharing our experiences, and comparing them to our expectations.

We began to consider how those expectations were initially shaped. We wondered how hatred is fueled between countries, pitting one against another, and how that hatred was sustained. One of our hypotheses was that the stories in the international press sparked or at least fueled the situation.

In a cosmopolitan city like Riyadh we had an array of international newspapers at our fingertips, and so we started a modest research project to compare news coverage from around the world.

We categorized the world press into four major regions: Western, European, Asian, and Middle Eastern. Neither of us is multilingual, but fortunately we found at least one English-language newspaper for every area we monitored.

Our news was bad news: as tentative and non-scientific as our "study" was, our findings were dismal. Coverage, even of the same issues, changed dramatically depending on the geographic source. We may think we're all on the same page when we read a newspaper, but we most definitely are not. We found ample misleading journalism, sometimes even outright propaganda!

Living in Riyadh, the most extreme differences related to stories about Israel and Palestine. Here's one example. When I opened a newspaper from the Middle East, the front page might show a large color photo of a slain Palestinian child or group of children injured by an Israeli rocket or firearm. When I opened a paper from the U.S., it would report an atrocity in which a Palestinian rocket landed on an Israeli village. Stories in the Far Eastern press generally had more emphasis on Palestinian views. We found British coverage fairly unbiased, providing a more neutral summary of happenings.

Another example was coverage of the United Nations. It was rare for American readers to find reporting about U.N. motions that reprimanded the U.S. or Israel about Middle East actions. Yet, in the international press, we found such articles once a month or more! To be fair, similar U.N. motions were made against Palestine, but these were much less frequent. What astounded us was that the American press simply didn't cover actions against Israel or the U.S. It got to where if we saw a report critical to the U.S. in a British newspaper, we'd immediately check the *New York Times*. Invariably we would come up empty-handed.

Different people will have different explanations for the causes of the different coverage. Perhaps it is simply the free enterprise system in the U.S.—if you think your readers won't buy your paper if you include certain stories, you just won't assign reporters to those stories. Whatever the reason, Mary Ann and I had a hard time accepting the apparent slant in coverage. The result plays into regional biases, nurtures stereotypes, and contributes to polarization and hatred around the world.

CHAPTER 27
Saudi Social

On a dry, hot evening (*Who am I kidding? Every evening was dry and hot!*) Meaghan arrived in Riyadh. She was on that same, surreal, middle-of-the-night flight Mary Ann and I had taken just a few months before.

Naif accompanied us to the airport and we all watched with eager anticipation as our abaya-clad youngest daughter strode down the hallway. Her eyes were shining, from exhaustion, disorientation, excitement, or all of the above.

Naif worked his paperwork magic as Meaghan effused about her flight. She had a long list of things she hoped to do while in Saudi Arabia during her spring semester.

I briefly updated her on my project's peaks and valleys. Mary Ann excitedly told her that she had arrived just in time for a social event she would find especially interesting: a Saudi-style party for women.

Mary Ann's friend, Wafa Al Sedairy, a gracious woman married to the Center's director, had invited Mary Ann and Meaghan to the party. It was to be a semiformal Chinese-themed affair, and Mary Ann was relieved that both she and Meaghan already had Asian-inspired outfits. *Thank goodness they didn't have to go on an extra shopping excursion.*

That Friday evening, the ladies in my life finished their preparations and gave me a brief fashion show. Mary Ann was ethereal, draped in a plum tunic and long flowing pants; Meaghan was radiant, clad in a vibrant jade green silk dress with a Mandarin collar.

At 9 p.m., we peeked through the curtains as a limousine slid up to our gate. Mary Ann and Meaghan hurriedly covered with abayas and darted to the waiting car.

They returned in the wee hours, giggling and whispering. I only pretended to be disgruntled at the pre-dawn wake-up call. They both were positively bubbling.

"OK, so first of all, in the limo, we met these really nice women," began Meaghan excitedly. "Some spoke English, some Arabic, and some both, so it was kind of hard to follow the conversation, but it didn't matter. Everyone was laughing."

Mary Ann chimed in. "We drove for fifteen minutes, arriving in this secluded and rather ritzy neighborhood. Terry, you and I have never been there. When we reached the Women's Club, one limousine after another pulled up to the entrance and deposited groups of happy, party-going, abaya-covered passengers. Just inside the building we were greeted, and we took off our abayas and checked them. Adorable young girls bade us welcome and waved incense. I guess it's a customary way to greet guests. The mezzanine-level entrance overlooked a huge room decorated as an Asian garden. Terry, you can't imagine how lovely it was!"

"Yeah," interjected Meaghan. "And can I ask something about our grand entrance? Why is it that all the women except for us seemed to float...how do they glide like that? Even up stairs! Like mom said, we were warmly welcomed...lots of kissing, both cheeks, of course, and laughing. Once we got inside, what a show! I wish you could have seen Mom," Meaghan said laughing. "She was hilarious; clutching her cloakroom claim ticket for dear life, knowing she'd never figure out which was *her* abaya in the sea of them at the end of the evening."

"Oh Terry, there was every type of dress and jewelry you could imagine!"

"And the women, Dad. I'm not sure why I was surprised, but most of them were professionals...doctors, dentists, social workers, teachers."

"And just like everywhere else in the world," Mary Ann added, "all the conversation covered women's universal topics: work, gentle digs about mothers-in-law, pride or concern about family, pregnancies, and disappointing haircuts. Except for the fact that everyone but us was olive skinned with dark hair and eyes, and spoke Arabic as much as English, I would have sworn I was in Madison. Meaghan, tell him about the belly dancing."

"Oh! There was a professional belly dancer, a woman with long dark hair and a stunning royal blue costume. She was awesome! But, what I loved the most is that so many women joined in! Some were really good dancers, most were just having fun, but it was so nice to see them letting loose. You know, when I imagined it here, I expected to see women modest and cloaked in abayas. It didn't really occur to me that I'd see gorgeous clothes, modern hairstyles, and stylish jewelry, and that they'd be joyful and free with themselves when only other women are around!

"And, Dad, you would have lost it seeing Mom and me at the end of the evening. We all headed to the cloak room to retrieve our abayas. Everyone else simply slipped them on, easy peasy. Mom and I struggled, our heads and necklaces getting caught every which way. We've got some practicing to do!"

Though it was late (or early, rather), we continued our conversation in the kitchen, comparing Saudi women's fashion to men's. *Or the lack of men's fashion, to be more accurate, since they all wear the same thing, all the time.* Again, I found it intriguing that women would spend so much time and money shopping for a dress no men (other than family) would ever see. Mary Ann seemed to have too much fun reminding me that even in the States, women dress up for other women, not for men. "Terry, men can be pretty clueless when a woman has gone to great pains to find an outfit that is just right. But her girlfriends, and especially her rivals, always notice."

She also explained that a Saudi mother "helps" her son choose a wife, and at social events like these, many of the older women are surreptitiously—or openly—collecting matchmaker data. The younger women know it, another reason for them to dress to impress.

Speaking of marriage, we learned much about the way Saudi weddings and nuptial arrangements can differ from those in the West. Now, there's no single way Saudi couples marry, but in the Dolan family's limited experience, it seems there are three common components: dowry, marriage contract, and public announcement.

We were honored to be invited to attend one wedding, and we learned more from talking to friends. Here are the informal findings from that research project.

First off, the parents may be the ones who propose. Well, by propose, I mean they may suggest to their child the name of someone he or she might consider marrying. Depending on how conservative the family, or the particular relationship, that may be the end of the conversation. *You are marrying Azam, and that's that*. Or, it may spark further discussion about potential spouses.

With rare exception, Muslims may only marry other Muslims. (It's ok if the prospective partner is a convert to Islam).

The dowry. To our knowledge, dowry discussions are conducted by the fathers of the couple. The negotiation includes details such as the size of the gift and the payment period. *Finance meets romance*.

Once the parents and children have agreed upon an appropriate marriage prospect, a meeting—a *shoufa*—is scheduled between the two families. It usually takes place at the bride's home and follows Islamic law. It serves as the prenuptial meet and greet.

You may be surprised to know—*I was*—that at the end of the shoufa, both candidates *(yes, the woman, too)* can veto the arrangement. And, we were told, dissolution of an engagement is not at all uncommon.

Given that Saudi Arabia can be a country of traditional male and female roles, Mary Ann was amused that the bride's culinary prowess never was even a consideration. In the Kingdom even modestly affluent families employ a cook and kitchen assistant!

Once the families have made it through dowry negotiation and shoufa, the couple signs a wedding agreement in a court of law. While that makes them *legally* married according to Islamic law, they are not publicly wed until a public ceremony takes place. The intermediary period is called the *milkah*; traditionally, the couple remains apart during this time. Allowances are sometimes made so they can be together to plan the wedding, shop for furniture, discuss—OK, argue about—the invitation list, etc.

The third component—the party—is the only one Mary Ann and I experienced firsthand, and we learned that wedding celebrations vary widely depending upon the socioeconomic status of the bride and groom. Some traditions are consistent though: the events are entirely gender-segregated events, and once again, it's the women who know how to have fun!

Sometimes the male and female events are held at the same time, but in separate rooms or locations. The men's party generally is a stately, subdued, sit-down dinner (depending upon how traditional the format, the meal may be served on a carpet with no table, chairs, or utensils or on a modern table with accompanying chairs, etc.) hosted by the groom's family. Food—whole goats or lambs, side dishes of rice, large baskets of dates, and fruit. Of course, the only libations are juices and water. The ceremony I attended included no speeches or even an inkling as to the nature of the function. I just as easily could have been at a Middle Eastern Rotary banquet.

The women's event for that wedding was much more elaborate!

I was told by Mary Ann, my Dolan family spy, "The bride's party was so much fun, Terry! There was celebration in the air and the women all were dressed to the nines."

Like the men's party, it was a sit-down dinner, but that's where the similarities ended.

Mary Ann described the scene. "The meal was delicious, served buffet-style, and the tables (with chairs!) were laden with china, silver, and beautiful linens.

"My tablemates told me that the women's party attendee list may vary from wedding to wedding, but it never includes men. Though you'll be interested to know, at one point in the evening, the groom and the two fathers made a brief appearance. When they did, the lights were dimmed so the female guests would be obscured."

She continued. "It would appear that the Western notion of a wedding party of bridesmaids and groomsmen is rare here in the Kingdom. But just like at home, the bride wore white. Sometimes she'll wear a special Arabic dress. There was live music at our party, sometimes it's taped, and sometimes, if the family is well-to-do, a special piece of music or poetry might be composed specifically for the bride and performed by the composer or author."

Mary Ann couldn't hide her amusement when she explained how mothers of unmarried sons blatantly "shopped" for potential brides among the attendees. Always in work mode, my mind imagined that many of the guests were from the same tribe or extended family, so these events were the birthplace of many a future consanguineous marriage!

CHAPTER 28
The Burden of Uncertainty

B y now I had learned quite a bit about Saudi marriage: the betrothal process, the ceremony, and other customs. I knew it was common to marry within one's tribe, even to marry one's cousin. However, I soon would learn something about marriage that never would have occurred to me.

My edification happened at a steering committee meeting. Seated at a conference table, the Minister of Health fidgeted with his notes and haltingly explained, "Dr. Dolan, our department recently uncovered findings from a previous study that likely will impact your newborn screening process." He didn't look pleased.

I placed my hands palms down on the table in front of me, braced for whatever new obstacle was about to come my way.

"Several years ago, in research unrelated to this project, we used a survey to determine the familial relationship between patients. We asked whether the husband and wife were first cousins, second cousins, or not related." He paused. "To our surprise, the research revealed that sometimes they didn't know. Or worse, they thought they knew, but it turned out they were mistaken."

With formidable restraint, I modulated my voice. "With respect, how can people *not* know if their fiancé is a first cousin? This would be the child of their mother's or father's own sibling!"

"Yes, I see how that might be hard to understand, Dr. Dolan, but here in Saudi Arabia, it is not as surprising. You see, marrying a first cousin here is not particularly noteworthy. And after generation on generation of marrying cousins, the specific nature of relationships sometimes becomes... well...murky. Please also remember that in many Saudi families, the bride and groom's parents may have upwards of twenty siblings, and subsequent family relationships become quite complicated."

I had just learned that married couples could not reliably tell us if they were first cousins. The possibilities for our own study were troubling, possibly disastrous. Yes, we hoped to determine if babies had inborn diseases, and the screenings and tandem mass spectrometry would help us assess that with certainty. But, we also sought to determine *causes* of these diseases. If we couldn't confidently assess consanguinity, we wouldn't know if the problem was caused by a genetic aberration or something else entirely. And, we couldn't provide informed advice about prevention.

So subjective data wasn't going to work for us. What could be Plan B? I could only hope we'd find an objective, scientific way to analyze parents' blood samples to determine consanguinity.

I was a man on a mission. Hastily gathering my notebook and briefcase, I perfunctorily thanked the Minister for this important information, and explained that I needed to start trying to find a solution.

I hightailed it back to my office to do research. First, I made phone calls to several geneticist colleagues to ascertain if they knew ways to find out the degree to which the parents of a newborn were related to one another. No luck.

An exhaustive online search followed my calls. I was surprised to find that studies on consanguinity in marriage were scarce. Moreover, the notion of using genetics to study the relationship between consanguinity and health of offspring was non-existent. *It's not always so exciting to be the pioneer.*

But wait, isn't it common knowledge that consanguinity and genetic abnormalities are linked? We know the familiar stories: hemophilia in some royal bloodlines; effects due to "inbreeding." It's true that there's ample anecdotal information and pop-culture assumptions, but at the time of our study, science was relatively silent on the subject.

One of the few studies I did find was conducted by a friend and associate, Dr. Brian Meyer, an Australian molecular biologist working at KFSHRC. He had evaluated the authenticity of questionnaire responses about spousal relationship by investigating actual family trees. His research suggested that up to seven percent of survey results regarding consanguinity could be wrong.[9] I did some more internet searches. Several

9 B.F. Meyer, "Strategies for the prevention of hereditary diseases in a highly consanguineous population," *Annals of Human Biology* 32 (2005): 174–179.

roads led to one person, Dr. Sam Samantha at the New York State Forensics Lab. The lab uses molecular genetics to identify human remains. *Forensics*?! With scenes from CSI running through my mind, I decided I didn't care. So what if the New York lab was renowned for identifying perps in grizzly crimes. If they could help us confirm consanguinity with a genetic test, I was in.

CHAPTER 29
The Green

I regularly worked late into the evenings. Occasionally I yearned for a scotch on the rocks, but settled instead for late night drives with Yahya and Mary Ann. We opened the Cruiser's windows, the night air surprisingly cool. *Relatively speaking.*

Whizzing down the highway, at every embankment we saw families, blankets spread, enjoying picnics. At midnight!

"Umm…Yahya, why are those people picnicking on the side of the road in the middle of the night? Isn't that dangerous? Or, at least, unpleasant?"

"It's the only grass," he replied. "And it's cooler now."

He was right, of course. With just a few exceptions—the landscaping in the DQ, an occasional golf course, these highway embankments—grass was a scarcity in Riyadh. And the temperature was incomparably more comfortable at this time of night, so why not picnic on the side of the road?

Later that summer, Mary Ann and I were awakened after midnight by the sound of children's laughter outside our villa. Just beyond our wall, an entire family enjoyed a picnic and playtime. This would happen time and again on the Thursday and Friday night Saudi weekends. It took some getting used to, but we came to look forward to the merriment of our temporary neighbors.

Speaking of grass, some of the most cherished growth in Riyadh was on the city's golf courses. I was fortunate to play on one of them, a full eighteen-hole course. It could easily give its American country club counterparts a run for their green.

This course, located a few miles outside the city limits, covered a beautiful plain and undulating hills, all dotted by palm trees. Much was identical to a Western course (including a grill featuring burgers and dogs), but some elements were quite distinctly Saudi.

First, because of the heat, each hole boasted elaborate drinking water facilities and abundant signage reminding players and caddies to stay hydrated. Another difference? I'd seen my fair share of sand traps, but until this course I'd never seen camels wandering through them! And the manner of these animals was hilarious. They pranced around with snooty entitlement as though they were gracing us with their presence. Heaven help you if your ball accidentally found the shade of a camel. It'd take some serious negotiating with the humped behemoth to find a mutually beneficial arrangement on how best to proceed.

Which reminds me of another animal anecdote. Early in our stay we learned that Saudi Arabia is a cat's Kingdom. Dogs are disliked and felines are fawned upon. In all our time in the country, we never saw a canine companion (the sole exception was the pet of an American expat couple). Mary Ann and I do not have strong feelings about cats, but we never got used to finding them everywhere, not as pets *per se*, but going about their business in gardens, picking through garbage, gallivanting wherever they pleased without so much as a mild "scat!" from the human residents. In Saudi Arabia, it is illegal to harm cats in any manner.

As plentiful as were camels and cats, one thing was even more so: dates on date palm trees. And they were delicious, the best we had ever eaten. We were blessed with several date palms in the Villa Dolan gardens. When I noticed they were in season, I asked our gardener, Anwar, if he might help us harvest the fruit.

One week later, we arrived home from an excursion to find every available surface in the house covered with dates. Dates in sealed plastic containers, dates in every space in our refrigerator. Dozens upon dozens of jars jammed our cabinets, cluttered our countertops, and perched precariously upon piles of books.

Mary Ann and I transformed them into date bread and three different kinds of date cookies. Dates circulated in our cereal, formed icing on our ice cream, and resided in our rice. Thankfully, the fruit is very healthy. Yet, as many dates as I ate, I never tired of them. To this day I still enjoy them, especially incomparable Saudi dates.

CHAPTER 30
Without a Cause

Back at the office the situation was far less fruitful. Reaching forensics expert Dr. Sam Samantha in New York proved difficult. He was a very busy man, much in demand, and even absent an eight-hour time difference, connecting would have been tricky. After several attempts, we did connect and I explained our conundrum.

"We are hoping to use blood samples from children and their parents to determine whether there is a familial relationship between the parents. Part of our study is to find out if consanguinity is a cause of inborn diseases and other problems."

Dr. Samantha agreed it was an interesting challenge. "Here's what we *can* determine with certainty. We can find out if the parents are *not* related, we can find out if they are siblings, and we can find out if they *are* related. However..."[10]

I realized I was holding my breath.

"However, with our current forensic capability, we cannot assess to what degree they are related. So, we can't tell you if they are first or second cousins, uncle or niece, etc."

He explained why not: The DNA scan that was available at the time assessed one to twelve DNA markers called alleles. Alleles are a gene or a portion of a gene involved in the inheritance of human traits. On screenings of two individuals, the more identical the alleles that show up, the closer the relationship between the people. If there are no alleles in common, it is very unlikely the pair are related. If all twelve alleles are the same, the two are siblings. The presence of some common alleles indicates some relationship, but we cannot determine anything more pre-

---

10 Sam Samantha, New York State Forensics Laboratories, Personal Communication, 2012.

cise.[11]

So close, but still so far. The news threatened to be a great defeat for our efforts. Like our colleague Dr. Meyer at the KFSHRC, we had to resort to a less satisfying Plan B or C or D...I was beginning to lose track of our obstacles and alternatives.

We couldn't scientifically, with one hundred percent accuracy, verify the relationship between the parents of a newborn with blood samples. So instead our team had to try to figure out the parental relationship through interviews and questionnaires during the screening process. Dr. Meyer's study told us a seven percent error rate was not uncommon. I'll never know how accurate our own efforts were, but I believe we were within a couple of percentage points of actual values—a "close-enough" statistic I'd have to live with.

Disappointed, I reminded myself and the team of the other important accomplishments from our newborn screening project: we had the ability to test and detect inborn errors; we had the ability to determine if the error matched one of fourteen diseases for which we were screening; and we had the ability to refer babies and children with these diseases for treatment. These were important "abilities." Our level of analysis treatment, while imperfect, was brand-new to the Kingdom and would save many, many lives.

But the scientist and the humanitarian in me yearned to do more, to take it further. I wished we could screen for more diseases. I wished we could determine if the causes were environmental, viral, bacterial, or genetic. The long range goals of our team were to strive in those directions, and eventually, we hoped to prevent the diseases from occurring in the first place!

Week by week, our team celebrated each time we crossed an item off the to-do list for our newborn screening program. And week by week, we renewed our efforts as new items took their place.

Heidi, I, and our modest crew at the Center dashed about. We felt like we were deckhands in a monsoon, tying an endless series of knots, hoisting sails to keep us afloat and moving forward. Deckhands on a tall ship, sailing across the desert.

The nature of the work quite literally was a matter of life or death for

---

11 Sam Samantha, New York State Forensics Laboratories, Personal Communication, 2012.

the Kingdom's children. Every day we labored with those children in our minds.

The workload was overwhelming. If not for Mary Ann and Meaghan, I may have taken up residence at the Center. But they provided me with happy respite and loving reasons to carve out time for life outside the PDSCR's walls.

CHAPTER 31
To Oman

S ummer neared. Meaghan and Mary Ann were going to return to the States for the summer, but first we hoped to explore more of the Middle East. We chose a brief vacation to Muscat, Oman, a popular destination among the Kingdom's expat community. The country was renowned for street art, historical sites, and friendly citizens.

Even from the skies as we flew in on Oman Air, Muscat was an impressive city. It nestled on the shore of Gulf of Oman, cozily situated between the Al Hajar Mountains and endless, endless desert.

Descending, we saw pale buildings and vibrant vegetation. Though the city boasts more than a million people, it was smog free and sparkling clean.

Shortly after landing, a taxi sped us to our hotel, passing statues and fountains at almost every intersection. Our small stately suite overlooked an oasis-worthy pool; and just a few yards past the pool, the sea.

A stone's throw down the beach was the U.S. Embassy and a U.S. Marines contingent. As we discovered, off-duty Marines were invited to enjoy the hotel's facilities. We felt unusually safe, though I did keep a father's watchful eye on my Meaghan.

We started with a guided tour of the city, and it dazzled us. We saw exquisite Moorish architecture, the grandiose Sultan Quaboos Mosque, and a remarkably unoccupied Qurum Beach. At the beach, Meaghan was the only one to brave a dip in the warm water.

Tuckered from sightseeing, we returned to the hotel. And, to my delight, a real happy hour. Alcohol is allowed in Muscat for non-Muslims.

Oman is slightly smaller than Kansas, and the primary industries are fishing, tourism, and, you guessed it…oil. We so enjoyed our tour of the city that we made arrangements for a driver to show us around rural

Oman the next day.

Our chauffeur Ahmed was in his early twenties and a new employee of the hotel. He had only recently moved to Muscat. With pride, and perhaps homesickness, he told us, "My village is small, but very beautiful, about an hour's drive from here. If you would like, I will take you there. Last night, I told my family, my parents and my two younger brothers and my little sister, that I'd be driving an American family today. They said they would be honored if you'd join them for tea." He continued excitedly, "You see, they have never met anyone from the United States."

We Dolan three nodded enthusiastically at one another, and I replied, "Yes, visiting your family and your village would be a treat for us, Ahmed. We've never seen an Omani home."

We drove on a highway, new but deserted. It brought us to a small desert village: single-story buildings, a hodgepodge urban plan completely bereft of traffic lights or greenery.

Ahmed pulled the car in front of a small, well-kept home. His family congregated in the foyer, anxious to meet us.

Mrs. Hamel was lovely, wearing what I envisioned was her Sunday (Friday?) best: an exquisite abaya and headscarf. Her husband greeted me with a hearty handshake; Ahmed's two brothers and sister, all formally dressed, simply could not contain their excitement. We entered the sparsely-furnished majlis, and Mr. Hamel invited us to take seats on cushions against the wall. The children perched just outside the door, mischievously peeking in the entire time.

It was hilarious (and a little disconcerting) how completely fascinated the Hamels were by us. In their eyes we felt like aliens from another planet, and they were transfixed. Mrs. Hamel, in particular, was completely absorbed with Meaghan, and sat closely next to her, staring unabashedly.

Only Ahmed spoke English, so conversation was slow. They peppered us with questions: "Where in the United States is your home?" "What are your professions?" "Is there much violence where you live?" "How many children do you have?" "Why are you visiting Saudi Arabia?"

They answered questions as enthusiastically as they asked them, and were clearly proud of their professional son who could now bring distinguished guests to their home.

While we talked, Ahmed and his parents took turns offering food and drink: sweet tea and home-baked biscuits. There were also oranges, which

Mrs. Hamel peeled and fed to Meaghan, one section at a time.

After an hour or so of a lovely visit, we expressed our profound thanks and rose to leave. A mere twenty minutes later, with smiles and *shukrans*, Ahmed led us back to the car. We returned to Riyadh the next day, relaxed and deeply satisfied from our first excursion.

CHAPTER 32
Mutawa Confrontation

My return from vacation was a rude awakening. The office seemed exponentially more hectic, perhaps because I had dared to escape. I wondered if it was worth the few days away.

At the Center my work resumed its fever pitch, and then some. Mary Ann and Meaghan returned to their daily lives in Riyadh. And then a run-in with a local mutawa, the religious police, erased their vacation-induced tranquility.

In the months that we'd been living in the Kingdom we had heard intimidating stories from our friends about run-ins with the mutawa, but we had not experienced it firsthand.

The mutawa, as noted previously, are members of an organization called the Commission for the Promotion of Virtue and Prevention of Vice. They aren't officially part of the Saudi Police Force, but the police provide them with lukewarm acceptance and support. When mutawa directives are disobeyed, even for seemingly trivial infractions, they find a real police officer to escort the accused to jail. According to the scant written materials available, they have three primary duties:

1. Ensure women are appropriately dressed per Islamic mores.
2. Keep unmarried men and women separate from each other. (Mutawa will often approach male/female pairs and ask for marriage documentation. If the couple cannot or will not produce the paperwork, they can be jailed.)
3. Ensure young men hightail it to a mosque at prayer times.

Generally, mutawa have little if any formal education; oftentimes, as has been noted in several public news sources, their interest in this role began with their own imprisonment. A jail stint includes compulsory memorization of the Qur'an, and sometimes when prisoners are released they have a newly acquired zeal for and adherence to Islam. So they become mutawa.

Bill Cornish and I often talked about a phenomenon we called the mutawa "teeter-totter." When relations between the Royal Family and the West seemed to be friendly and the Wahhabis were angry, the mutawa sensed they could be more aggressive because the Royal Family would not want to stir the pot. And when the Royal Family seemed to veer conservative, citizens showed less patience for—and more public complains about—the mutawa, which tempered their aggression.

Mary Ann and Meaghan's mutawa melee took place in a local mall. The Dolan women were relaxing after some shopping and lunch. Mary Ann inadvertently allowed her head cover to slide, and a bit of blonde hair poked out. She had been distracted by a group of boisterous high school boys making rude comments to Meaghan. Aggravated, the two made their way toward the exit to find Yahya and their ride home.

Suddenly, from across the mall, a visibly angry member of the mutawa (easily recognizable by shorter-than-usual thoubes and longer-than-usual beards) rushed toward them shouting, "Cover your hair, woman!"

Initially, Mary Ann ignored him, believing he was accosting them for no good reason. *Mistake*. He charged toward her with a vengeance. Mary Ann and Meaghan knew he wouldn't deign to touch an infidel female, no matter how angry he was, so they didn't feel physically threatened. But they knew that nothing good would come from a confrontation with an angry mutawa. As Meaghan shared with me later, "So many Americans wrongly assume we are exempt from local laws when we travel. That's just not true."

Mary Ann instinctively positioned herself to protect her daughter. Meaghan just wanted to skedaddle, with as little fuss as possible. With Yahya just ahead, Meaghan adjusted Mary Ann's head cover, took her arm, and let Yahya briskly usher them to the waiting car.

Safely inside, crisis averted, the women in my life exploded with anger, each for a different reason.

"Arrrrggh! I'm so angry. That was just ridiculous!" exclaimed Mary Ann. "Why did you pull me away? Those high school boys can shout inappropriate comments to you, that's not a problem for the mutawa. But heavens, a bit of my hair was showing, and that's cause for alarm!"

Meaghan responded with her own anger. "Mom, we could have been arrested! You *know* this wasn't the time or place to pick a fight about what is right or wrong with the system here. You made the choice to live here. Are you going to change the entire country? And do it all in one day?"

Meaghan sighed, calming down a bit. "Look, I know how angry you are. I am, too. And we are entitled. But being mad isn't going to help anything. We can't take this personally. And we can't change all this. All we can control is our own reactions."

A quietly seething pair returned to Villa Dolan that evening.

Several months later, I'd have a once-removed mutawa run-in of my own. Not far from the DQ was a small flower shop run by a kindly Lebanese gentleman. Mid-morning on Valentine's Day I stopped to purchase long-stemmed red roses for Mary Ann. He was unusually brusque, telling me he had no roses. But then he discreetly winked and whispered, "Stop by later." I was perplexed, but did return on my way home from work. Sure enough, he was back in his usual good spirits, and brought me a dozen lovely roses. He explained. "The mutawa stormed in this morning and confiscated all my red roses. They didn't want infidels," and he smiled, gesturing to me with a nod, "to purchase them with sinful intent." They assumed they had taken them all, and they left. "Luckily," he said, and cleared his throat conspiratorially "I had 'forgotten' a supply, and now they are yours."

CHAPTER 33
Meaghan's Report: Women and Youth

One of the reasons Meaghan came to the Kingdom was to see what life was like for young Saudi women. Not surprisingly, young people were more likely to talk frankly with her than they would with Mary Ann and me.

Meaghan routinely shared her observations with us. As her visit drew to a close, we asked her for a more complete description of her impressions.

Teens and young adults comprised two-thirds of the Kingdom's population. Meaghan explained that "it really doesn't come as a surprise that young people are eager for change, they always are, but to me, it's not necessarily as a cry for democracy. I think they just want more supportive and flexible leadership."

Her assessment was that young men seemed far more dissatisfied, even antagonistic, than their female peers, and I agreed. The young men rebelled against their parents more, and some had scant interest in education or employment. For instance, every weekend a group of young men in souped-up vehicles gathered on main shopping boulevards, revving loudly, racing in and out of traffic recklessly, and daring the local police to intervene. Even the mutawa seemed cowed by their dominant and aggressive behavior.

That group represented a minority, though. Most youth were not outwardly angry or defiant; nevertheless, they did seem dissatisfied. They were clearly constrained by some of the cultural rules imposed upon them.

Some of Meaghan's friends, she said, used social media to meet boys or girls. "Even though this is kind of rebellious," she explained, "they still are dedicated to school, especially the girls I met, and they are committed to finishing their university studies." Though many had elders who pressured them to "find a husband and raise a family," education was a high priority for girls: a means to better themselves, gain employment, and become productive citizens.

As I mentioned, though, with the exception of three universities—King Abdul Aziz University of Minerals and Petroleum, King Abdullah University of Science and Technology, and Princess Nourah University—most Saudi schools emphasized religious studies and neglected science, technology, and other curricula that would better position students for careers.

We mustn't forget that the U.S. and Western Europe took hundreds of years to develop great universities, and Saudi Arabia is less than a century old. Growing pains are to be expected, and the three aforementioned schools are an excellent start.

Meaghan asked young women how they felt about the country's restrictions: forced to cover, not allowed to drive, prohibited from accompanying an unrelated male. She told us that "most of my friends don't really mind the abaya and headscarf—you have to remember they've worn them every day for most of their lives. They told me that even though they have to cover in public, they can be pretty free and open among other women.

"But, they can't stand that they are not able to drive!" Meaghan said with a laugh. "They told me that they know it's a way of life, but it's a way of life that is inconvenient and requires complicated logistics."

With regard to mixing genders, Meaghan said that some of her new friends thought it was silly that they couldn't spend time with boys, but others didn't seem to mind.

With the exception of a minority of angry young men, Meaghan found that most Saudi youth, including young women, did not feel as constrained by the country's conservatism as we Westerners imagine. "We can't view *their* experience through our own beliefs—if we do, we get a skewed picture," she said. While the Kingdom's youth may strive for change, they were, at least in Meaghan's observations, relatively accepting of their culture and customs. Girls especially were eager to learn, to pursue careers, and to raise families. Some hoped to travel or study in other countries, including the United States, but many were content to remain in the Kingdom.

Summer brought inferno-like heat along with departures, Meaghan permanently and Mary Ann temporarily. They bade farewell, preparing to leave Riyadh together. Both would summer in the States with friends and family. Then Meaghan would travel to Spain for fall semester at the University of Seville.

My plan was to return to Madison briefly toward summer's end with Dr. Mohammad Rashed, the scientist who would become our Mass Spectrometer Screening Director in addition to his duties as the NBS Director at the KFSHRD. Mary Ann, Dr. Rashed, and I would return to Riyadh in mid-September.

CHAPTER 34
Somber Summer

I continued at the Center during the sweltering Saudi summer. *Thank you, indoor air conditioning.* Mary Ann and Meaghan delighted/taunted me, regaling me with jaunts to Madison's famous Farmers Market, refreshing dips in Lake Mendota, bacon and other pork indulgences, concerts and plays, and time with friends.

Mary Ann also used the summer to catch up on medical checkups. She had a decades-long relationship with her physician and preferred not to start over with a new practitioner in Riyadh.

It was during a family reunion in Mitchell, South Dakota, that the news came.

Mary Ann was visiting her family at her mother's apartment. Everyone wanted to see her abaya, so she drove back to her hotel to retrieve it. When she returned to the apartment, abaya in hand, she found deeply concerned looks on her family's faces.

While Mary Ann was away, her physician had phoned and left a message saying Mary Ann should call upon her return. She did. The news: there was an abnormality on her mammogram and further tests were needed. The doctor reassured Mary Ann that no lump was present, but rather a possible cellular anomaly. She returned to Madison for a biopsy and the result confirmed her doctor's suspicion. Mary Ann had early, cellular breast cancer.

Though Mary Ann and I talked almost daily, it was wrenching for us to be so far apart while all this was happening. We were so grateful to our children who helped ease this difficult time for us. I left Riyadh to be back in Madison for her surgery.

Thankfully, Mary Ann's procedure went well. Her doctors were confident the cancer was removed, but advised a course of radiation. She planned to return to Riyadh with me and to receive treatment in Saudi Arabia.

The morning of our flight, we awoke to clear blue skies and sunshine. We were scheduled to depart from Dane County Airport later in the day. As we tucked clothes, books, and toiletries into our suitcases, the telephone rang. It was our daughter Elizabeth, urgency in her voice.

"Mom! Oh thank goodness you're still there. Have you seen the news?"

"No, I was just packing. What's going on?"

"Turn on the TV. You aren't going to be able to fly today."

Phone in one hand, remote in the other, Mary Ann turned to the TV. On one channel, images of a plane crashing into the World Trade Center. Another channel: another plane, the second tower. Another channel: flames, smoke, dust, and debris. People running, noses and mouths covered. Firefighters. Police. Mayhem.

Mary Ann immediately telephoned me. I was with Dr. Mohammed Rashed, the expert I was recruiting for our newborn screening program. We, like the rest of the country and the rest of the world, sat disbelieving in front of TV sets.

Mary Ann spent the new few hours trying to reach friends and family, especially those scheduled to fly that day. We were particularly concerned about colleagues who might be en route to or from the Middle East. Thankfully, there was only one, and he and his wife had already landed safely in New York.

Around the world, flights were grounded.

The world as we knew it had changed forever.

In those few days following September 11, 2001, we didn't know what the future held. No one did.

Perhaps because he held an Egyptian passport, Dr. Rashed was able to fly back to the Middle East twelve days later. Mary Ann and I didn't know when Americans would be able to resume air travel, especially to Muslim countries. We didn't know what political climate awaited Americans in Saudi Arabia—we didn't know if we would be allowed back, and if so, if we'd be welcome.

In the face of all these uncertainties, Mary Ann had to focus on her health. She heeded her doctor's advice to begin an immediate radiation course. Because our fate in Riyadh was unclear, she decided to stay in

Madison for a few months to treat her cancer. If and when it was ok for me to go back to the Kingdom, I would; she would join me when her treatments were complete.

CHAPTER 35
Return to Riyadh

Heidi held down the fort during my absence. She and I were in contact every day so I could stay current on progress at the Center, and we developed contingency plans in case it was impossible or inadvisable for me to return.

Naif and I also communicated daily. During these tense days, he assured me on Prince Sultan's behalf that my return would be warmly and safely welcomed once planes were flying again. The all-clear came at the end of the month, and I headed to Riyadh. I was eager to return to the newborn screening project, but also a bit anxious and uncertain.

I knew Mary Ann was in good hands. Our cadre of friends and family would take good care of her, but I was worried about her. Even though Mary Ann is a trooper, radiation is a difficult and exhausting experience. I couldn't wait for her to return to Riyadh in a few months when her treatments were complete.

And, while I was reassured by Prince Sultan's confidence about my return to the Kingdom, I was hesitant about my role as an American scientist in the Middle East in the post-9/11 world. But work has its own agenda, and during the long series of flights from Madison to Riyadh I decided to focus on our next immediate steps. We needed to move the newborn screening project forward. I would think about what I *could* effect, rather than worry about things I couldn't.

I was surprised how quickly my life in Saudi Arabia returned to "normal." I missed Mary Ann and Meaghan, of course, but I had already spent the summer without them. I returned to my familiar too-many-hours-at-the-office routine.

I felt like I never had a free moment, but Heidi took on a workload nothing short of amazing. Along with our HR director, she oversaw recruitment of all the staff needed for every aspect of the program, including technicians to staff the microscopy lab and master's-level social workers to run the training programs at birthing sites. Hundreds of positions needed to be filled, then the new hires needed to be trained.

During this recruiting frenzy, Heidi also fine-tuned and distributed all the training materials ultimately destined for parents and clinicians.

Our steering committee of seven continued to meet on an almost-weekly basis. Our well-balanced blend of experience and personalities ensured on-the-ground tactical know-how and high-level strategic perspective. Plus, we enjoyed having well-informed conversations with each other. Each meeting was instrumental in pushing the program closer to reality.

Before long, the laboratory was staffed, social workers were added to our roster, and we had inked the contract with the overnight shipping service. Planning, staffing, logistics—many months and many accomplishments passed by.

Our stalwart team continued apace and we built a newborn screening program from the ground up. Months whizzed past. Before long, around the time we celebrated our third year in Saudi Arabia, all of the program's systems were ready to go: hundreds of birthing centers across the Kingdom were staffed and trained; the mass spectrometry laboratory had personnel and equipment; and transport to major cities, small towns, and even Bedouin villages was arranged. It was time for the program to launch. I had two other tasks. One was administrative—to identify a successor for my position—and one was monumental—to actually pass along the supervisory baton and return home to the States.

I found a superbly qualified replacement in Dr. Steven Schroeder, a colleague and friend from the University of Kansas and the past director of the Mental Retardation Research Center there. After introductions and interviews with Prince Sultan and our oversight committee, Dr. Schroeder was heartily approved to assume my duties.

Mary Ann and I began preparations to take leave of our adopted country. I reflected on the threads my team had formed and woven together: The Prince Sultan Center had blossomed; the newborn screening program had slowly but steadily grown in size and prominence; the PSCDR was buzzing and packed as a beehive. In three years, the number of staff working on PSCDR projects had nearly tripled. Truly remarkable progress happened during the years we were in Riyadh.

CHAPTER 36
Prepare for Departure

In the weeks prior to leaving, Mary Ann and I spent quiet time together, usually in the early morning over coffee or in the evening before bed, reflecting on our Saudi Arabia experiences. It was a time swirling with mixed emotions.

We couldn't wait to see family and friends back home. An occasional international telephone call didn't satisfy the way hugs and kisses do. And, I'm not ashamed to admit, visions of Western cuisine, particularly Mary Ann's meatloaf wrapped in pork bacon, did a little jig in my head.

Yet our hearts were filled with almost palpable loss to leave such a significant and joyful phase of our lives. We went through a roster of names, newfound friends we would terribly miss.

I remember telling Mary Ann that residing in the Diplomatic Quarter felt unlike anywhere else I'd ever lived. Our neighbors hailed from dozens of countries and spoke many languages. I struggled to explain it to myself. "It's like living on an island in the middle of an archipelago. You and I live on one island. Our friends live on nearby islands of their own. The space between our islands is sometimes calm and sunny, sometimes tumultuous. Crossing the waters can be risky, and successful navigation depends upon following inscrutable directions, conveyed in a language we don't understand." Mary Ann tilted her head, gave me an odd little look, but nodded in agreement. Then she added "And because crossing is always so unpredictable, it feels kind of perilous, and when you finally reach a familiar island with friendly faces, it feels like a haven...every single time."

I reached across and squeezed her hand.

Mary Ann and I reminisced about time spent with our new friends, with my colleagues, and with the Prince. We remembered the first time we heard about this opportunity, and the incredulous exhilaration we felt about embarking on our daring adventure. Looking back, we realized it was every bit as wild and wonderful as we hoped it would be. This journey transported us to places we never would have seen, and it exposed us to truths about the world, and about people, we never would have learned. We experienced occasions that simply could not be replicated. And we developed friendships and memories that will be with us forever.

We both hoped we would return. *Inshallah*! (God willing!)

It was our last week in Riyadh; we reveled in a cavalcade of professional and social events. There was a dinner party or neighborhood gathering almost every night and numerous other events during the days.

At the Center, much of the activity had two focuses: drawing closure on some of our research, and preparing for the arrival of Dr. Schroeder. An accomplished scientist, leader, and administrator, he was about to enter a surreal new environment—similar to my own entrance just a few years prior. Thanks to Heidi and our administrative staff, we knew they would make his transition as welcoming and as smooth as possible.

The highlight of the week, held the day before our departure, was a party hosted by the entire PSCDR staff. Standing around in the Center's open-air atrium, many people gave speeches, both lighthearted and poignantly heartfelt. I was especially touched recalling our very first meeting several years before—when Heidi and I faced suspicious, solemn faces and absolute silence.

Today, many proudly stated that their PSCDR job was the most exciting of their career, that they had never felt so integral to a team, and that they knew they were a part of something important and far-reaching. Our female staff members were especially effusive in their gratitude, telling how exceptionally rewarding it was and that they had never felt more valued.

Maya Raffi, always the spokesperson on behalf of the women, regaled the group. "I don't think Dr. Dolan fully appreciates the special role he made possible for us and the independence that he granted us. This was truly a great experience we shall not forget."

Our staff presented us with traditional thoubes, created especially for Mary Ann and me. Years later these gifts, always on prominent display in our home, never fail to spark discussion among our guests.

Finally, this occasion gave me an opportunity to recount for the staff the significant accomplishments we had achieved.

"You'll recall," I began, "that only three years ago we had only thirteen employees, none women." I nodded and smiled at Maya. "And lots of vacant offices." Today, we have an on-site staff of more than thirty, almost half women, and upwards of one hundred twenty-five people at outreach sites around the country.

"I came, and Dr. Al Askary returned, to Saudi Arabia with three primary objectives: to oversee the establishment of a national research center so the Kingdom could increase research on developmental disabilities; to launch a critically-needed, national, newborn screening program to assess the health of newborns and young children; and to develop concomitant treatment and educational programs on their behalf. I am proud to say we accomplished each of those objectives.

"In developing this Center, one of our major accomplishments was creating our Extramural Funding program so scientists from all over the Kingdom can submit research applications." Although this was a standard practice in many Western countries, it was somewhat of a new experience in the Kingdom, particularly in the support of research and understanding of developmental disabilities.

"As a result, many of you had to expend major efforts," and I smiled at the appropriate staffers, "to counsel scientists on how to submit these documents. By year two your work enabled us to support several research projects: studies of lead exposure in young children; studies of delayed speech and language training; studies of delayed motor development; studies of children with Autism-spectrum disorders; and more. Because of you, for the first time ever in this country, the Kingdom's scientific community began pursuing relevant and important research on children.

"In just under two years, we had an action plan for the newborn screening program, and agreements for support from the KFSHRC and the Ministry of Health. As you know, KFSHRC has been a particularly valuable partner. Through these partnerships, we created specialized technical plans and genetics laboratories capable of examining each of the Kingdom's births.

"And now, at the end of three years, we have a group of scientists and clinicians throughout the Kingdom at the ready to examine, diagnose, treat, and support newborns and young children with inborn errors and related autosomal genetic diseases. I'm talking about one hundred birthing sites across the country and personnel and equipment to transport hundreds of thousands of samples each year to Riyadh for testing.

"It is a hope I share with you that the program will be able to treat every infant born in the Kingdom's future.

"Finally, and perhaps most important, we initiated research and discussions, among health professionals and lay citizens about the possible causes of autosomal diseases. And we set the groundwork for developing future preventive measures."

I paused and looked around the room at each and every face, one by one.

"Because of your tireless work these past three years, we have ensured that developmental diseases are studied, screened, evaluated, and treated throughout the land. Babies will be safer, families will be happier because of your contributions.

"Thank you."

The silent room erupted with applause. Saudi "champagne" flowed freely.

It was a glorious day.

But if I learned one lesson during my stay in the Kingdom, it was to expect the unexpected.

The phone rang. One of my associates, the one nearest the phone, grabbed it and cheerfully answered. His face fell ever so slightly as he passed the phone to me, saying, "The Immigration Ministry. It doesn't sound good."

I took a deep breath, put the phone to my ear, "Dolan here."

Farewell party or not, it would appear we were not leaving Saudi Arabia after all. The Immigration Ministry denied our application for departure.

Is it April First? No, it wouldn't matter...April Fool's Day isn't big in Saudi Arabia. Is this a prank? These were my distracted thoughts as I listened to the bureaucratic monotone on the phone. He told me, slowly and in great detail, that the Ministry's records indicated that Meaghan, who had departed from the Kingdom a couple years prior, was still in the country. It would appear her *igama* had never been returned. An igama is the official Saudi document that permits a visitor to stay in the Kingdom. When one leaves the country, the paper must be returned to immigration officials. Typically it is removed from the passport at the airport upon departure.

My irritated reply that "Meaghan departed two years ago. I assure you she's not hiding in the desert!" was met with silence. I said I would clear things up and hung up. Then I immediately placed a call to Meaghan to ask her to check for the igama; indeed, it was still pasted inside her passport. Evidently, the airport officials neglected to retrieve it from her. I called back the Immigration Ministry to point out that it was actually their mistake. I learned, not for the first time dealing with a bureaucracy, that accountability does not equal responsibility. It was up to us to produce Meaghan's igama or stay in Saudi Arabia.

Other than using a few choice Arabic words I learned, I didn't know what to do. My shoulders slumped. From jubilation to tribulation in just three calls.

But, then, of course, the solution came to me in a flash. Why hadn't I thought of it before? I think I may actually have slapped my own head. *Must have been the Saudi "champagne,"* I thought with a smile. *Went straight to my head.*

I called the Solver of All Problems, Prince Sultan. Within hours, a seemingly insurmountable obstacle had simply evaporated. Mary Ann and I were cleared to depart the next day.

On our final afternoon as residents of Riyadh, I walked over to the office of HRH Prince Sultan. Images from our first meeting and memories about his kindness and tenacity flooded me with emotion at each step.

As was his manner, he invited me to sit on a large wingback chair in his office. At a small ornate table between us immediately appeared the inevitable coffee.

Prince Sultan began, clapping me on the shoulder, "Dr. Dolan, my friend, what a journey this has been, is it not so?"

"Your Highness, it truly has been."

"Do you remember," and he chuckled heartily at the memory, "Do you remember that vigorous discussion we had years ago when with great and admirable zeal you insisted that we hire women on the PSCDR staff?"

"How could I ever forget?"

"I just want you to know, Terry, that every time I visit the Center, I am impressed with the staff's *esprit de corps.* I believe that the morale and staff satisfaction engineered enthusiasm and dedicated to the Center's mission."

"Thank you, Your Highness. It means so much to me to hear you say that."

"Terry, I also want to tell you that I know that sometimes the tensions between the efforts of the Center and some of our more...'conservative religious members'...may have made your efforts more difficult, more trying. But I want you to know that this project has been a boon to the entire Kingdom, to countless children and families. Terry, I am overjoyed with our tremendous progress."

"Prince Sultan, none of this would have been possible without your vision and commitment. A few short years ago you suspected there was a problem and you set all this in motion. Today, we have a system in place to confirm your suspicions and move towards a remediation of that national circumstance.

"And, this has been an extraordinary opportunity for Mary Ann and me. We have been part of something transformational and we both have become so close to our staff and our Saudi friends. You know, before we arrived, I feared we'd be 'Strangers in A Strange Land.' But that did not happen, Your Highness. The past few years here have been deeply satisfying, both personally and professionally.

"When I think back to my time here, it will be with joy. I know our work will screen millions of children and will help thousands overcome diseases. In my mind's eye I can see smiling, happy faces, the faces of all the children of the Kingdom."

PART III

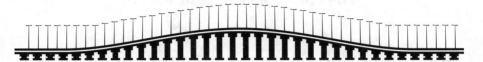

CHAPTER 37
The Coffee Server's Son, Part III

*P*recisely *three days later, and for the first time during his tenure, the Coffee Server asks his supervisor a personal favor—to use the telephone to make an important call. The employer is curious, but gives permission with no questions. At the appropriate hour, Ibrahim enters an unused conference room, closes the door behind him, and carefully dials the number to the clinic. He is put through to Dr. Al Zahrani, who has a voice uncannily similar to Ibrahim's grandfather. A promising sign.*

"Ibrahim," the doctor begins, "The news I have for you is hopeful. We expect your son Aziz to be just fine. He has tested positive for a disease called biotinidase deficiency. This is a disorder he inherited from you and your wife, even though neither of you has any symptoms yourself. His body does not make an important enzyme called biotinidase, so he cannot process the vitamin biotin. That results in some of the symptoms you have seen such as seizures, weak muscle tone, breathing problems, and more. You and your wife did the right thing by bringing him to be tested. Thankfully, this is a highly treatable disease when it is caught in time. Ideally, we like to detect this at birth, but in Aziz's case we are lucky. The problem has progressed slowly. Your boy will need a simple daily supplement, the biotin enzyme, for the rest of his life, but it is not expensive, it won't hurt him, and you can get it at any pharmacy. Mr. Maloof, your son is going to be just fine."

Ibrahim audibly breathes a sigh of relief. "Dr. Al Zahrani, thank you for this wonderful news. Aziz will be alright, Alhamdulillah." But, one question remains. "Dr. Al Zahrani, may I ask… my wife and I have been fearful about having more children. Will they be sick as well?"

"It is possible, but not certain. If more babies come, you must noti-

fy your wife's doctor about Aziz's condition when she is expecting, and make certain that each baby participates in the newborn screening project when they are born. The earlier we catch the disease, the better the chances your babies will be fine."

"Shukran! Shukran, Dr. Al Zahrani."

Ibrahim gently replaces the phone and looks at the clock on the conference room wall—two more hours and he can return home to his wife with wonderful news.

CHAPTER 38
Progress at the PSCDR

Despite the focus on the efforts of the Newborn Screening Program, notable other progress was being made at the PSCDR. Upon our arrival in the Kingdom, it was clear that there was a modest—at best—national effort to conduct research on developmental disabilities. It was also clear that there was a minuscule national effort to promote and fund such endeavors. Although there was a national funding program (KAST) that served as the country's National Science Agency, a perusal of its activities indicated little activity involving children with disabilities. Our PSCDR staff therefore decided to initiate our own effort to meet those needs.

We organized an extramural research program to begin financing projects in these areas. PSCDR sought and accepted research applications from investigators throughout the land (almost all would be university-based scientists), reviewed their applications for scientific merit, and then funded the most meritorious proposals. Admittedly, the program had a slow start (it was after all quite a novel concept for many of the behavioral scientists), but within a year the program was well energized and the Center received nearly two dozen applications worthy of support. The projects studied such things as children exposed to high levels of lead, children with autism or autistic-like syndromes, and children exhibiting delayed development—including motor, sensory, and perceptual skills; cognitive skills; speech and language skills; and classroom skills of various kinds.

Progress in the Newborn Screening Program also was impressive. We knew we were constrained by the occasional limitations of science and technology. We also knew we could not absolutely identify consanguineous marriages and neither were we able to assess a correlation between consanguineous marriage and the incidence of inborn errors. Still, we were able to draw conclusions with the methods and data available to us.

Here is a summary of the number of children screened by the project:

Year	PSCDR	Ministry of Health
2006	50,000	
2007	90,000	
2008	98,000	
2009	107,000	
2010	112,000	
2011	117,000	
2012	138,000	
2013	52,000	146,000 (est.)
Total	764,000	
Grand Total:		910,000

In the gender-segregated culture of Saudi Arabia, here is a view of a conference audience with the men to the right and women to the left

The dias of a scientific conference in Riyadh. The person in the center is a Saudi Arabian chairman while those on the left and the right are Americans.

Women gather during the interlude at a scientific conference in Riyadh.

Men gather during the interlude at a scientific conference in Riyadh.

While attending a scientific conference, I was interviewed by the Saudi press during the tea break.

Mary Ann and I in a typical Arabian majlis, a sitting area for greeting guests but always gender segregated.

A scene from the fish market in Muscat, the capital of Oman. The city is a most impressive urban area, highlighted by magnificent sculptures and art on many street intersections.

An inlet in Oman.

Our Omani driver (left of Mary Ann) during our tour of Oman invited us to his family home out in the desert in central Oman. His parents had never seen anyone from America. They were completely fascinated with Meaghan.

Meaghan and Mary Ann overlooking the rough terrain in Oman. Like in Saudi Arabia, the inland areas of Oman are a mixture of mountainous and sand deserts

Vegetables anyone? Note that the attire of non-Saudi Muslims is an all-white robe and not the Saudi Arabian thoube.

Shopping at the carpet souk. From the left: Drs. Jack and Sue Chandler, the Dolans, and the carpet dealer. Jack Chandler was the Director of the King Khaled Eye Specialist Hospital in Riyadh, the main eye hospital in Saudi Arabia. Meaghan was shopping for a Middle Eastern carpet—a memento gift from her parents.

Ah, Starbucks…the world over! Mary Ann and Meaghan were most appreciative.

Saudi coffee and treats are served to spectators at the camel races. The camel "track" was several miles long and a race was a lengthy affair.

Robert W. Jordan

The Ambassador of the United States of America

requests the pleasure of your company

at a Ramadan reception

on Sunday, December 2, 2001

from 9:00 p.m. to 11:00 p.m.

| *Regrets Only* | *Quincy House* |
| 488-3800 Ext. 1262 | *Ambassador's Residence* |

An invitation from the Honorable American Ambassador to Saudi Arabia for a Ramadan reception.

Meaghan and Mary Ann dressed for a party with other Westerners.

A party at the American Base outside of Riyadh. The person in the middle is Dr. Brian Meyer, an Australian, a dear friend, and a superb scientist.

Meaghan and a friend inside the Syrian embassy.

The Syrian embassy in the DQ. The architecture, typical of many of the embassies, was baroque and quite elaborate

CHAPTER 39
Efforts in Other Middle Eastern Countries

A s part of the preparation for our program in Saudi Arabia, we examined efforts throughout the region. We discovered that *more than half* of marriages in Jordan, Qatar, Yemen, Kuwait, and the United Arab Emirates, were between cousins. Our hypothesis was that Saudi Arabia, like these other countries, would exhibit genetic diseases at rates higher than would be expected for countries with lower percentages of consanguineous marriages.

If we could show a relationship between rates of consanguinity and incidence of genetic disease—that is, if countries in the Gulf with high rates of consanguinity demonstrated greater levels of genetic disease—that would provide validation of our hypothesis.

Some countries had already implemented successful newborn screening programs, so we had the benefit of the best practices from those countries. In 1995, the Emirate of Dubai was among the first countries in the region to launch such a program. In 2014, the *Eastern Mediterranean Health Journal* reported that the Dubai programs began screening solely for phenylketonuria, and over the years built up to screening for sixteen diseases in ninety-five percent of infant births. Dubai credited its program's success to superior education and outreach, dedicated staff, excellent and dependable laboratory analyses, thorough follow-up, effective management, and comprehensive evaluation. In all fairness, however, it should be noted that the other countries in the Middle East are typically a fraction of the size of Saudi Arabia with a fraction of the number of births per annum.

In 2007, Qatar also began a modest but promising screening program. The most significant hurdle for Qatar is a lack of technological facilities: the program has partnered with Heidelberg, Germany, some 6,000 kilometers away, to conduct clinical measurements.

There are other new programs. Bahrain has a program to screen for sickle cell anemia and Egypt has a program to screen for congenital hyperthyroidism. Other efforts, still small in scale, are being reported in Oman and other countries.

CHAPTER 40
A Note About the Future

At the Center, I recently presented my final assessment of the maternal and child health care profile in the Kingdom and the outlook for the youngest generation. In my report I concluded that some of the most dramatic and positive occurrences happening now are changes in Islamic religious codes and tenets. Many of these changes have taken place during this past decade and are ably described and discussed by Dr. Aida Al Aqeel in two manuscripts.[12]

In her discussions, Dr. Al Aqeel points out that as a result of these Saudi Arabia has encouraged research in several important and effective ways: it has approved a new national science and technology development plan, it has committed 1.6% of the nation's GDP to research and development; and it is investing approximately $2 billion in higher education institutions with research centers. Also, Kuwait has set up a small genetics center, and the United Arab Emirates is in the process of building one. However, the number of relevant experts in these countries is still limited.

These advances are related to the Kingdom's efforts to enhance its technological and scientific capacity. Dr. Al Aqeel and other scientists have also discussed the changes happening at the intersection of science and religion. *(Because of the importance of my interpreting Dr. Al Aqueel's writings with exactitude, I have summarized her liberally from the two papers referenced above.)*

The religion most relevant to *our* discussions is Islam. While Islam is viewed by much of the world as an Arabic religion, in fact there are

---

12 Aida I. Al-Aqeel, "Ethical Guidelines in Genetics and Genomica: An Islamic Perspective," *Saudi Medical Journal* 14, no. 12 (2005) 1862–1870; and Aida I. Al Aqeel, "Islamic Ethical Framework for Research into and Prevention of Genetic Diseases," *Nature Genetics* 39, no. 11 (November 2007).

millions of Muslims living in African and Asian nations. Further, more than half of North American Muslims have been born to families long resident rather than to immigrants; most of those long-resident families are African-American although there are an increasing number of Muslim converts from Caucasian and Latino families. I have read in several journals and news articles recently that Islam is, by some margin, the fastest growing religion on earth. It doesn't surprise me.

Fifty-seven nations belong to the Organization of the Islamic Conference, and that conference represents a wide range of guidelines for religious interpretation of scientific and medical judgments. Many religious and scientific experts usually weigh in on these judgments, and intense and broad discussions are involved. These deliberations do not always result in consensus, and individuals may select their view of choice, often the one they believe aligns most closely to the teachings of the Qur'an. However, no particular view is binding, and each nation has its own jurisprudence processes.

I found some surprising recent views and rulings pertaining to contraception and sterilization. I am informed that in Islam, contraception methods are acceptable if they are temporary. That means sterilization is not acceptable unless the life of the mother is threatened by a pregnancy. Further, if the mother already has had two or more congenitally-affected babies, the norm is that the mother usually finds legitimate approval for use of sterilization.

To me, one of the most significant changes in the accepted views of many Muslims is the role of abortion. When I first moved to the Kingdom in 2001, my understanding of genetic intrusion rules was that the fetus could not be "touched" from the moment of conception to the moment of birth. All strategies dealing with the health and well-being of the fetus involving direct interaction with the fetus were forbidden as long as the fetus was within a woman's womb.

My reading of some more recent views accepted within members of the Muslim faith are that, under extreme circumstances, abortion of the fetus can be acceptable. Specifically, "according to Islamic teaching, human life begins at the time of *nafakh al rouh*, inspiration of the soul, which in the Holy Qur'an and Sunna is stated to be at the 120th day after the moment of conception."[13] As discussed further, before that moment the embryo has sanctity, but has not yet reached the status of a full human

---

13 Ibid.

being. Prenatal diagnosis and abortion is allowed before the 120th day of gestation if the fetus has a condition that would be a calamity for both the family and itself; those conditions do *not* include Down syndrome or certain other conditions, such as thalassemia. As a result, abortions because of serious fatal congenital disorders can be–and are–carried out in some Muslim countries, including Tunisia and Iran. However, according to the fourth fatwa of the Islamic Fiqh (Jurisprudence) Council of the Muslim World League...abortion is also allowed after 120 days if there is a danger to maternal life without regard as whether the fetus is abnormal. In these cases termination of pregnancy goes against religious well-being, but it is done, acceptably, for the mother's physical health.

Adoption—as we define it in the West—it is not allowed in Islam. However, similar practices to our adoption are practiced in Saudi Arabia, but is descriptively and legally comparable to our foster programs. Practices vary from country to country in the Midddle East, but fostering within some families and orphans is common.

There is a technique that has stimulated much discussion in Saudi Arabia and elsewhere—pre-implantation diagnosis. It was introduced in the mid-1990s as an alternative to prenatal diagnosis. The technique involves in-vitro fertilization with the intent of evaluating the health of the fertilized egg. A healthy, fertilized egg—free of defects—is placed into the womb. Although the technique can be abused (e.g., sex selection), it is highly useful for some couples to assure a healthy fetus despite a history of abnormal offspring. This program was sponsored originally among scientists at the PSDCR and the KFSHRC.

Perhaps the most important issue to our project, emerging in the past decade, is the growing number of screenable diseases. Our initial estimates in 2000, based on data from Western countries, were fifty potentially-screenable diseases (our initial approval was for fourteen). Remarkably, as reported by Dr. Al Aqeel in another paper[14] it is now estimated that perhaps 150 varieties of neurodegenerative diseases can be detected through screening programs, including many autosomal recessive disorders or prenatal disorders unique to the Middle East. And, science has been able to find the precise molecular defects associated with many of these diseases. Combined with policy changes that have been made by

---

14 Aida I. Al-Aqeel, "Common Genetics and Metabolic Diseases in Saudi Arabia," *Middle East Journal of Family Medicine* 6 (2004): 96.

Islamic leadership, prevention of many of these diseases will now be possible by either pre-implementation genetics or prenatal diagnosis.

For the leadership of the newborn screening project in the Kingdom, these changes and discoveries will help them expand the program's scope.

To my mind, the recent modifications suggested by the multi-national Islamic Council represent a genuine re-balancing between religious and medical considerations. When I first arrived in the Middle East in 2001, the rule that a fetus was "out of bounds" was a religious dictate; it was not a dictate in recognition of opportunities to better serve the health and well-being of the infant. In just ten short years, Islam is moving toward a stance that recognizes modern science and medicine without offending any religious considerations. That movement can result in great good for the life and well-being of infants and children. To me that has been a great step forward in the Middle East as it determinedly moves forward on behalf of all humankind.

AFTERWORD
As this edition goes to press in 2016...

Prince Sultan bin Salman's father has become The Custodian of the Two Holy Mosques / King Salman bin Abdul Aziz. Although Prince Sultan's life undoubtedly has changed with his father's ascension, the Prince has continued to be an indefatigable leader and ally in the field of children's health.

Before my office phone rang on a spring morning back in Wisconsin, children born into the Kingdom entered a country of noted prosperity, but also entered a country with limited national healthcare programs for children. A member of the Royal Family of Saudi Arabia changed this forever. He was—is—a visionary, a man of seemingly unlimited skills, among them, leadership and steadfast tenacity in the face of challenge.

The families of every child saved by the newborn screening program owe thanks to Prince Sultan bin Salman bin Abdul Aziz.

Dr. Heidi Al Askary transferred from the PSCDR to the Human Resources Development Fund where she assumed another mammoth effort. She now directs a national program to create employment opportunities for people with disabilities. She is a capable and perceptive leader, one who recognizes that employment for these individuals is another mountain to be scaled for the betterment of humankind.

Dr. Sultan Al Sedairy and Dr. Ali Al Odaib continue in positions of leadership at PSCDR. Following Dr. Schroeder's tenure, Dr. Sedairy assumed acting directorship of the PSCDR in addition to his duties at the KFSHRC. Dr. Odaib now serves as director of the newborn screening program. In addition to the prodigious duties of directing this program, he will provide leadership (along with the Ministry of Health) to modify and expand the mission of the program in screening and treating additional diseases.

Bill Cornish, who had been enormously helpful to me, has since retired and moved to the United States.

The adventure I have described touched the entire Dolan family. Meaghan's Saudi Arabia experience changed her life. Following completion of her baccalaureate from the University of Wisconsin and a graduate degree at the Elliott School of International Affairs at George Washington University, she is working with critical language programs at the Institute of International Education. In this role she helps prepare multilingual candidates for positions in international affairs. She is making a notable contribution; Mary Ann and I could not be prouder of her or happier for her.

Saudi Arabia has left an indelible impression on Mary Ann and me. I continue to travel to Saudi Arabia to provide counsel, make occasional speeches, and monitor activities. I try and take advantage of any opportunity to spend time and work with Prince Sultan. On occasion, I also consult with countries and Emirates that neighbor the Kingdom with respect to their efforts on behalf of children with disabilities. And I spend much of my time writing about our experiences in the Middle East. Mary Ann is my partner, by phone or over coffee, in all of these activities. She is an unparalleled aid in helping me recall our Saudi Arabian experiences, and helps edit written materials. Perhaps most important, she has become an advocate for positive relations between the U.S. and Saudi Arabia, and takes every opportunity to educate and correct misperceptions Americans have about the Kingdom and Islam.

Note: This is a memoir. It is based entirely on my memory of events and of the participation of friends and colleagues in those happenings. To the extent there are errors in my memory, I apologize to all individuals affected.

Secondly, to the degree possible, I have named correctly every participant involved in the activities described in the events. I have assumed that, given the historical nature of the manuscript, permission of the actual use of their names was not required.

APPENDIX
Newborn Screening Project Diseases Screened

- Phenylketonuria (PKU)
- Maple Syrup Urine Disease (MSUD)
- Arginosuccinase Deficiency (ASL)
- Citrullinemia (ASD)
- Hg-CoA Lyase Deficiency (HMG)
- Isovaleric Acidemia (IVA)
- Methylmalonic Acidemia (MMA)
- Propionic Acidemia (PA)
- Beta-ketothiolase Deficiency (BKT)
- Glutaric Acidemia type-1(GA-1)
- Medium-chain acyl-CoA dehydrogenase deficiency (MCAD)
- (3-MethylCrotonyl CoA Carboxylase deficiency (3-MCC)
- Galactosemia
- Congenital Hypothyroidism (CH)
- Congenital adrenal Hyperplasia (CAH)
- Biotinidase Deficiency
- Very Long Chair Fatty Acid Dehydrogenase Deficiency (was added in 2014).

One of the positive aspects of this list of screened diseases as selected by Saudi Arabia is that, for the most part, early detection (i.e., at birth) can have dramatically positive results. Several of them, for example, are amenable to positive treatment outcomes using one of the following easily-implemented strategies: close parental monitoring, medications, dietary supplements, fasting and special diets, hormonal treatment, antibiotic prophylactics, and parental education (e.g., attention to early-warning signals).

BIBLIOGRAPHY

al-Abdulkareem, A.A., and S.G. Ballal. "Consanguineous marriage in an urban area of Saudi Arabia: rates and adverse health effects on the Offspring." *Journal of Community Health* 23 (1998): 75–83.

Abdulrazzaq, Y.M. et. al. "A study of possible deleterious effects of consanguinity." *Clinical Genetics* 51 (1997): 167–173.

Ali, Jasim. "Saudi Arabia's continuous efforts to tackle unemployment." www.GulfNews.com. Al Nisr Publishing, LLC, 3 May 2014.

Applegarth, D.A., J.R. Toone, and R.B. Lowry. "Incidence of inborn errors of metabolism in British Columbia: 1969–1996." *Pediatrics* 105, no. 1 (2000): 10.

Baird, P.A., A.D. Sadddovnick, and I.M.L. Yee. "Maternal age and birth defects: a population study." *Lancet* 337 (1991): 527–530.

Benner, A., and K.A. Alali. "Consanguineous marriage in a newly developing country: the Qatari population." *Journal of Biosocial Science* 38 (2006): 239–246.

Bennett, R.I. et. al. "Inconsistencies in genetic counseling and screening for consanguineous couples and their offspring: the need for practice guidelines." *Genetics in Medicine* 1 (1999): 286–292.

Bittles, A.H. "Consanguinity and its relevance to clinical genetics." *Clinical Genetics* 60 (2001): 89–98.

Bittles, A.H. "Endogamy, consanguinity, and community genetics." *Journal of Genetics* 81 (2002): 91–98.

Bittles, A.H. "The influence of consanguineous marriage on reproductive behavior in India and Pakistan." In *Diversity and Adaptability in Human Population*. Oxford: Oxford University Press, 1995.

Bittles, A.H. "The role and significance of consanguinity as a demographic variable." *Population and Development Review* 20 (1994): 561–584.

Bittles, A.H. "When cousins marry: a review of consanguinity in the Middle East." *Perspectives in Human Biology* 1 (1995): 71–83.

Bittles, A.H. et. al. "Human inbreeding: a familiar story full of surprises." In *Ethnicity and Health*. London: Taylor and Franis, 2001.

Bittles, A.H. et. al. "Reproductive behavior and health in consanguineous marriages." *Science* 252 (1991): 789–794.

Bittles, A.H., and M.I. Black. "Evolution in health and medicine." Sacklet Colloquium: Consanguinity, Human Evolution, and Complex Diseases. *Proceedings of the National Academy of Science*, supplement (2010): 1779–1786.

Central Department of Statistics and Information. Official Report. Kingdom of Saudi Arabia, 2013.

Chace, Donald H. "A Layperson's Guide to Tandem Mass Spectrometry and Newborn Screening." Technical Report. NeoGen Labs, 1997.

al-Essa, M., P.T. Ozand, and S.I. al-Gain, "Awareness of inborn errors of metabolism among parents in Saudi Arabia." *Annals of Saudi Medicine* 17, no. 5 (1997): 562–564.

Fathzadeh, M. et. al. "Genetic counseling in Southern Iran: consanguinity and reason for deferral." *Journal of Genetic Counseling* 17 (2008): 472–479.

al-Gazali, L.I. et. al. "Consanguineous marriages in the United Arab Emirates," *Journal of Biosocial Science* 29 (1997): 491–497.

al-Gazali, L.I. et. al. "The profile of major Congenital Abnormalities in the United Arab Emirates (UAE) population." *Journal of Medical Genetics* 32 (1995): 7–13.

al-Gazali, L.I., H. Hamamy, and S. al-Arrayad. "Genetic Disorders in the Arab World." *BMJ* 333 (2006): 831–834.

Hamad, Waleed Al Bu Ali et. al. "Risk factors and birth prevalence of birth defects and inborn errors of metabolism in Al Ahsa, Saudi Arabia." *Pan African Medical Journal* 8 (2011): 14.

Hamamy, H. "Consanguinity marriages: preconception consultation in primary health care settings." *Journal of Community Genetics* 3 (2012): 185–192.

Hamamy, H. et. al. "Consanguineous marriages, pearls and perils: Geneva International Consanguinity Workshop Report." *Genetics in Medicine* 13 (2011): 841–847.

el-Hazmi, M.A. et. al. "Consanguinity among the Saudi Arabian population." *Journal of Medical Genetics* 32 (1995): 7–13 and 623–626.

al-Hussain, M., and M. al-Bunyan. "Consanguineous marriages in a Saudi population and the effect of inbreeding on perinatal and postnatal mortality." *Annals of Tropical Paediatrics* 17 (1997): 155–160.

Hussain, R. "Community perceptions of reasons for preference for consanguineous marriages in Pakistan." *Journal of Biosocial Science* 31 (1999): 449–461.

Jurdi R., and P.C. Saxena. "The prevalence and correlates of consanguineous marriages in Yemen: similarities and correlates with other Arab countries." *Journal of Bioso-*

cial Science 35 (2003): 1–13.

Koury, S.A., and D. Massad. "Consanguineous marriages in Jordan." *American Journal of Medical Genetics* 43 (1992): 769–775.

Lindner, M. et. al. "Implementation of extended neonatal screening and metabolic unit in the State of Qatar: developing and optimizing strategies in cooperation with the neonatal screening program in Heidelberg." *Journal of Inherited Metabolic Disease* 4 (2007): 522–529.

Mishkin, Sarah. "Saudi Arabia to use FedEX web course to train unemployed." *The Financial Times*, 15 July 2014.

Moammar, H. et. al. "Incidence and patterns of inborn errors of metabolism in the Eastern Province of Saudi Arabia." *Annals of Saudi Medicine* 30 (2010): 271–277.

Modell, B. and A. Darr. "Science and society: genetic counseling and customary consanguineous marriage." *Nature Review Genetics* 3 (2002): 225–229.

el-Mouzan, Mohammad I. et. al. "Regional variations in the prevalence of consanguinity in Saudi Arabia." *Saudi Medical Journal* 28, no. 12 (2007): 1881–1884.

el-Mouzan, M.I. et. al. "Consanguinity and major genetic disorders in Saudi children: a community-based cross-sectional study." *Annals of Saudi Medicine* 28, no. 3 (2008): 169–173.

al-Odaib, A.N. et. al. "A new era for preventive genetic programs in the Arabian Peninsula." *Saudi Medical Journal* 24, no. 11 (2003): 1168–1175.

Ozand, P.T. "Diagnosis of inborn errors of metabolism by tandem mass spectrometry." *Annals of Saudi Medicine* 18 (1998): 234–239.

Rashed, M.S. et. al. "Screening blood spots for inborn errors of metabolism by electrospray tandem mass spectrometry with a microplate batch process and a computer algorithm for automated flagging of abnormal profiles." *Clinical Chemistry* 43, no. 7 (1997): 1129–1141.

Saad, F.A., and E. Jauniaux. "Recurrent early pregnancy loss and consanguinity." *Reproductive Biomedicine Online* 5 (2002): 167–170.

Saavedra, Carlos A. Personal Communication, March 2013.

Sandridge, A.L. et. al. "Consanguinity in Qatar: knowledge, attitude and practice in a population born between 1946 and 1991." *Journal of Biosocial Science* 42 (2010): 59–82.

Teebi, A.S., and T. Farag. "Genetic disorders among Arab populations." *Oxford Monographs on Medical Genetics* No. 30. New York: Oxford University Press, 1997.

Teebi, A.S., and S.A. Teebi. "Genetic diversity among Arabs." *Community Genetics* 8, no. 21 (2004): 115.

ACKNOWLEDGMENTS

On a cold November morning, a few months after our final return to the United States from Saudi Arabia, Mary Ann and I were enjoying breakfast in a neighborhood diner. Sitting at the counter next to us was a stranger, a somewhat senior gentleman who, during the course of breakfast, was continually approached by friends who congratulated him. We learned that in his retirement he had published a book, his first one: a novel about youth.

Myles Golde is his name, and he and I started to talk about the genesis and process of his experiences of becoming an author. My lasting memory of that conversation was the extraordinary satisfaction shining from his eyes because of his accomplishment. It was at that moment I decided I wanted to be one too—I wanted to join the kingdom of authors.

Luckily, I started my new life as an author surrounded by capable and very intelligent people. Fellow scientists and colleagues, many more experienced than I, listened to my thoughts and even read my drafts.

Fred Wightman, my go-to colleague in many aspects of science and a lifelong wise and valued friend, has been involved in every aspect of the final document, conceptually and editorially. Also, Stephen Schroeder, my successor in Saudi Arabia, was a critical thinker and reader who provided key leadership. William Cornish was a source of valuable information on countless occasions and helped keep me on the straight and narrow.

I was also aided by a cadre of family and personal friends who read various drafts: Meaghan Dolan; Mitchell Kenoian; Charles Smith; William Yost; my brother, David Dolan; Michael Knoche; Ansley Bacon; David O'Hare; my sister Jacqui Miller; and Myles Golde. Afra Sumeir, a long-time resident of Saudi Arabia, was particularly helpful in reviewing text related to the culture and religion of the country.

The faculty and staff of the Newborn Screening Program at the Wisconsin State Screening Laboratory and the Waisman Center at the University of Wisconsin-Madison were also helpful. Sandy Van Calcar, who has since transferred to a position in Oregon, was most helpful in providing a written description of the inborn errors we were pursuing in the Middle East. In addition to her important assistance, other members of the faculty and staff associated with the Newborn Screening Program in the State of Wisconsin who provided valuable information included Dr. Gary Hoffman, now retired; Dr. Greg Rice; Dr. Patricia Held; and Dr. Jessica Sott Schwaerer.

Finally, Dr. Sam Samantha of the New York State Forensics Laboratories helped bring me up to date on several issued related to the relationship between genetics and consanguinity.

It is inevitable there are others whom I am momentarily forgetting. I hope they will understand how grateful I am to them.

I also express my gratitude to Sharon Woodhouse, the first member of the publishing community to express interest in my efforts and who continues to serve as a valued agent and advisor. Also, Milestones, The Gift of a Lifetime, a writing and editing service, played an important role in the development of the text. One of their colleagues, Andrew Pacelli, was particularly helpful. Finally, Tracy Marks of Beyond Words and copyeditor Michael Green were critical to the development of the final edition, as was designer Todd Petersen.

I would be remiss if I didn't thank my family. Our youngest daughter Meaghan spent much time in the Kingdom and was an invaluable member of our family team. Our other children—Katherine Lazar, Patrick Dolan, and Elizabeth Dolan—were supportive and encouraging throughout the process. Mary Ann, my number one everything, was my number one editorial assistant, source of countless suggestions and the main cog in my memory.

I save my last thanks to two individuals who made the entire saga possible: HRH Prince Sultan bin Salman and Dr. Heidi Al Askary. Prince Sultan is the leadership, energy, and force behind the KSCDR and the newborn screening program in Saudi Arabia. At times, it was he alone who kept the program alive. He is truly a lynchpin in many Saudi Arabian issues including the health care of children with disabilities, and tourism and antiquities.

Without Dr. Al Askary, this program would not have succeeded. It was a stroke of uncanny luck to discover her as a student just about to begin her professional career. She is intelligent, highly energized, and extraordinarily talented. Heidi is a leader in the Kingdom's future.

Note: This book is a memoir and a tribute. To the best of my ability, all persons are named as I met them, and I express my profound appreciation to them all and apologies to the few I may have forgotten.

—TRD

Prince Salman and author Terry Dolan.

INDEX

Page references in italics indicate illustrations. "TRD" refers to Terrence R. Dolan.

ABOUT THE AUTHOR

Terrence R. Dolan is Emeritus Professor of Neurology and Psychology of the University of Wisconsin-Madison and the Past Director of the Waisman Center on Developmental Disabilities and Human Development. The Waisman Center is one of the largest research centers in the world on human development with an emphasis of the biological and behavioral components of development in children. Previously, he conducted research in child psychology with a particular interest in brain mechanisms and processes underlying communication.

After a twenty-year tenure at the Waisman Center, Dr. Dolan was contacted by Prince Sultan bin Salman bin Abdul Aziz, a prominent member of the Royal Family and the son of the recently-crowned King of Saudi Arabia. Prince Sultan and several colleagues suspected there was a growing incidence of serious if not fatal diseases among the Kingdom's children. In their view too many babies exhibited diseases that were severe and incapacitating. Because of Dr. Dolan's expertise developing and managing large research centers, he was recruited to assist in the development of a national research center in Saudi Arabia to gather new knowledge and understanding of childhood diseases and disabilities.

Terrence Dolan is currently retired and lives with his wife in Wilmette, Illinois, near several of their four children and seven grandchildren.